Pony's Girl
Parables

BY DEBORAH DRAVES LEGG
ILLUSTRATED BY STEVEN C. LEGG

Pony's Girl Parables

By Deborah Draves Legg

Illustrated by Steven C. Legg

Copyright © Deborah Draves Legg

ISBN: 978-1-7378773-1-8

Designed and written by Deborah Draves Legg

Illustrations: Steven Carl Legg

Edited by George Verongos

First edition published 2021 by Eponicity, LLC

Contact: Deborah Draves Legg - www.eponicity.com

Eponicity, LLC.

Other published work by Deborah Draves Legg includes the poetry collection, *Aligning – Partnering with Soul* (2021).

This book is dedicated to Juano, Dorado, Gitana, and Beauty. You are forever a part of me, as I am part of you.

Δ∇Δ∇Δ∇Δ∇

And to every horse that has carried me, body and Soul, on this pilgrimage. Thank you.

Δ∇Δ∇Δ∇Δ∇

And to the love of my life, my husband, Steven.

Table of Contents

Acknowledgment i

Foreword iii

Introduction v

Chapter 1: The Ambassador – Potential Unfolding 1

Chapter 2: The Seer – See Unconditionally 9

Chapter 3: The Balancer – Choose Truth 25

Chapter 4: The Sensor – Live Connected 41

Chapter 5: The Co-Creator – Two Aligned Are More Than the Sum 53

Chapter 6: The Processor – Emotional Resilience 65

Chapter 7: The Protector – The Right to Be 77

Afterword 85

Appendix 89

    Chapter 1 - Expanded 89

    Chapter 2 - Expanded 95

    Chapter 3 - Expanded 105

    Chapter 4 - Expanded 111

    Chapter 5 - Expanded 117

    Chapter 6 - Expanded 123

    Chapter 7 - Expanded 131

Bibliography 137

About the Author 139

Acknowledgment

"When the student is ready, the teacher will appear..."
– Tao Te Ching

Alan Seale is the founder of The Center for Transformational Presence. An inspirational leader and gifted teacher, he has opened the gateway to, as he says, "what wants to happen" for countless people. People ready to begin their pilgrimage of remembering who they were born to be.

In *Pony's Girl Parables*, the Ambassador, Seer, and Co-Creator archetypes are based on Alan's work, as are some of the subtle messages in the parables.

Alan, thank you for being an Ambassador, being the light, and guiding me to mine.

Δ∇Δ∇Δ∇Δ∇

My husband, Steven Legg, and I met in 2003. In 2006 we left our life in the USA and moved to Costa Rica. Against all odds, we transformed an old dairy farm into a popular resort at the base of an active volcano. During our 14 years in Costa Rica, we experienced a lifetime of memories. Some of these stories are woven into *Pony's Girl Parables*. Thank you, Steve, for bringing to life, in the illustrations, what I imagined in my mind. Together we are more than the sum.

Δ∇Δ∇Δ∇Δ∇

i

Foreword

Deborah and I met on a trail ride she was leading from her Leaves and Lizards Retreat facility in Costa Rica. To her, I was probably just another tourist; but when I fell off my horse Titan into the River Arenal, she probably saw me as an insurance risk! After that ride, I shared with Deborah that I had spoken with her horse, Titan, and he had a message for her. Most people would likely have dismissed me at that point, categorizing me as "crazy." Not Deborah. She listened, and she acknowledged that the message was about something I had no way of knowing other than from the horse! Our relationship grew from there, and over the ensuing years, I took equine-facilitated learning workshops with Deborah and wrote *When the Horses Whisper*. This book documents conversations I had with 11 of her horses.

From being with Deborah and her horses, I have seen and understood parts of myself that I'd never known. And I've observed many people open their hearts and expand their consciousness as a result of Deborah's equine-facilitated work. Most inspiring has been to watch how gently, yet directly, she reaches children through encounters with horses. For example, I was visiting Leaves and Lizards when Deborah was working with a group of young girls who were victims of forced child prostitution. It was heart-wrenching to see the heaviness of these girls on their arrival, and all the more miraculous to see them as they left; a transformation and healing process had begun as the result of their encounters with Deborah and her horses.

Deborah is a nurse and spent several decades caring for newborns in neonatal intensive care units. She is also an equine-supported therapist and professional coach. The combination of these skill sets, plus her inner work, gives her the capacity to reach a wide range of people struggling with life traumas, challenges, or those simply yearning for a deeper sense of themselves.

Pony's Girl Parables is an insightful and illuminating set of teachings, accessible to young readers and adults. I would not have guessed Deborah would bring her gifts to writing as another approach to her healing work; however, I am delighted she has done so in this creative and deeply powerful book.

Rosalyn W. Berne, Ph.D.

Author of *When the Horses Whisper* (2013),
Waking to Beauty (2016),
Waiting in the Silence (2015)

△▽△▽△▽

Introduction

"Owning your own story and loving ourselves through that process is the bravest thing that we will ever do."
— Brené Brown

This book is about remembering who we were born to be. One day in early 2019, while organizing files on my computer, I stumbled across an article I had downloaded but hadn't read, by Alan Seale, called "Soul and Ego – The Fundamental Partnership." It was perfect timing for my next teacher. Here is an excerpt of that article:

> *Ego understands how the physical world works. It knows all about the rules and structures of daily life because all of those rules and structures were designed by egos in order to create a space in which egos can live together in relative accord. However, ego knows nothing of the vast, unseen, non-physical realms of the greater Consciousness. In fact, it has a great fear of those realms because to ego; they are completely unknown.*
>
> *Soul, on the other hand, knows nothing of the rules and structures of daily life, yet is totally at home in the vastness of possibility, the incredibly vast realm of Consciousness, and with exploring the unknown. Without ego as the physical component of being, soul cannot have a life in the physical realm. And without the expansive awareness of soul, ego lacks inspired direction.*

So soul needs ego in order to have a physical world experience, and ego needs soul for the "big-picture" view.

At least once in your life, you have probably experienced being incredibly excited about a big step you were about to take—perhaps a trip to a new part of the world, a career change, a big investment, a move to a new city, or country. Your soul was eagerly anticipating this step and the new possibilities available once the step was taken. Yet just as you were finalizing your plans or were about to take the plunge, a voice inside screamed, "Are you crazy? Do you realize the risks you are taking?" Perhaps that voice went on to say things like, "You're going to lose all your money," or "Your husband will never go along with this," or "People will think you've lost your mind," or any number of arguments ego will make in its desperation to keep you in a space and way of life that it perceives to be safe.

In those moments, if we don't understand both the limited awareness of ego and its deep need for security, as well as the bigger vision of the soul, we may, unfortunately, retreat from our great adventure and talk ourselves out of the very thing that the soul was longing for. And as we return to the "safe" life where things are known and predictable, deep inside, it feels as if a part of us dies."

The day of my epiphany, after reading Alan Seale's article, I had an equine coaching session with a family: a mother, father, and their 10-year-old daughter. I soon discovered this session was just as much for my benefit as theirs.

I selected two horses to work with; Dorado and Beauty. I started the session with Dorado and left Beauty tied up outside on the rail. The parents were seated outside of the arena while I began the session with their daughter, let's call her Suzy. I didn't have a plan; over the years of working with horses in this way, experience has taught me it's better not to have a plan; it's best to let the horse lead the session, revealing what wants to play out.

This session was not her first time around horses; as part of the experience, I reviewed some simple techniques, how to use the child-sized whip, and standard safety considerations when around horses. We stood in the middle of the arena; Dorado was at liberty (not tied up). He chose to stand next to us, yawning, licking, and chewing, a signal he approved of the content in my lesson. When horses yawn, lick, and chew, it indicates that they, or the client, have shifted from a state of unsureness to a state of understanding.

After I finished talking, Dorado moved to the outer edge of the arena; I understood it as a hint that he wanted Suzy to move him around the arena to practice using the whip. I demonstrated how to move him in a circle by pushing energy behind him with the whip without touching him, using the whip like an energy wand that he moves away from. Soon she was ready for me to step back; I moved out and sat on the rail, allowing her to continue the interaction with Dorado by herself. Shortly, when it was just the right time, Dorado stopped moving and stood like a statue in the corner. Every effort she made did not move the horse.

"What is happening in there, Suzy? What does Dorado want you to notice?" I asked.

"He reminds me of me when I have to do my homework." Her parents nodded in agreement; schoolwork was the issue at hand.

"What motivates you to do your homework?" I questioned.

"When my parents give me treats, then I'll do it," she replied.

"Do you think if you gave Dorado a treat, he would cooperate with you?"

"No, that won't work; he'll just eat the treat and still stand there." She was a wise little girl.

Beauty, still tied outside the arena, started banging her hoof on the gate. I tried to ignore her, but she was insistent. Taking the cue, I went over and let her in to wander inside with us at liberty. I returned to where Suzy was standing. Without provocation, Beauty started running around the arena. She was beautifully cantering around and around us. Dorado, the living statue, stayed in the corner.

"Suzy, what does Beauty want you to know? What is she showing you?" I asked.

"Beauty is my spirit." She smiled. "Dorado is the worker part of me, and Beauty is the spirit part of me."

I was stunned. Here it was, Ego and Soul playing out right in front of me through a 10-year-old girl. It seemed as though my heart grew a size.

"How can they work together?" I asked.

"I don't know, let me think." She looked at Dorado. "I want to ride him."

"Ok, good idea." I saddled Dorado; Suzy put on a helmet and got on. She had been on several rides already while staying at our retreat center and was a good rider.

"Suzy, I want you to get Beauty to follow behind you and Dorado. Discover what it takes to keep your spirit connected to the worker part of you; that is your challenge," I coached her.

She rode Dorado around for several minutes, coaxing Beauty to tag along, but she would have none of it; she ignored them and wandered around the arena in disinterest.

"I need to ride Beauty now, so I can understand what she wants." Just as she said that Beauty walked up alongside Dorado, I moved the reins over to Beauty; Suzy hopped right from Dorado's saddled back to Beauty's bareback without dismounting. She tried to get Dorado to follow them; he wouldn't. Eventually, she gave up and just enjoyed riding Beauty around the arena for a while. I played a song for them on the Bluetooth speaker. Silently, we watched them moving in harmony to the music; the two seemed to blend into one.

After the song ended, Suzy seemed to have gained some clarity about the goal I had given her. "I want to change to Dorado again." Dorado, taking the cue, positioned himself next to

Beauty, and Suzy hopped back in the saddle. They walked off, and Beauty followed. I played another song; we witnessed the three become one.

When the song ended, she rode up to us on Dorado with Beauty at her side. "I know what my spirit wants," she smiled and looked at her parents, "she wants me to do my homework, that is what makes her happy. The reward for doing it does not come from you or my teacher, it comes from here," she pointed at her heart, "it comes from inside of me, that is where my spirit lives. I'm a kid; it's my job to be a student right now."

What gifts I had received; a living demonstration of the fundamental partnership between Soul and Ego and a meaningful parable-like story for me to tell.

$$\Delta\nabla\Delta\nabla\Delta\nabla\Delta\nabla$$

A parable is a short story that often illustrates a universal truth. It usually contains a familiar character that faces a moral, ethical, or challenging dilemma. Parables can be a platform to discuss difficult or complex ideas by expressing an abstract argument in a storytelling narrative.

As an equine-facilitated learning instructor and Transformational Presence coach, I often find myself working within the context of parables. Parables are experiential and thought-provoking, like working with horses; experience produces a lasting impact. Coaching sessions with horses often evoke metaphorical interactions that reach us in profound ways. These metaphors are deeply seeded within our psyche, emerging as aha moments or self-reflective *knowings*. Once we *know*, we cannot unknow what was summoned up from our psyche.

Metaphors are rooted in our stories, often experiences passed down from our ancestors. Human civilization was founded on stories. Before scientific explanations, stories provided some theory as to how the world worked. Stories helped form our diverse cultures and the ethical framework for group consciousness. Stories as parables share wisdom without preaching, allowing us scope to relate to the content on a personal level. We can read a parable as a child, glean one message, then reread it as a teenager or young adult, and other concepts surface. As adults, parables remind us to philosophically reflect upon our own lives, maybe even our reason for being. *Pony's Girl Parables* are the stories of my life's adventures, my pilgrimage of remembering the Ambassador I was born to be.

Δ∇Δ∇Δ∇Δ∇

The chapters of *Pony's Girl Parables* are centered around seven archetypes: The Ambassador, The Seer, The Balancer, The Sensor, The Co-Creator, The Processor, and The Protector. Some readers will notice another layer of insight embedded into each chapter that corresponds to our chakra system. I think of the chakra system as part of the software that runs the hard drive, our body.

In her book, *Eastern Body, Western Mind: Psychology and the Chakra System as a Path to the Self*, Anodea Judith describes the chakras as a "center of organization that receives, assimilates, and expresses life force energy." She describes them as "spinning spheres of bioenergetic activity that emanate from the major nerve ganglia branching forward from the spinal column." The seven major chakras are stacked in a column of energy that run from the base of the spine to the top of the head. It has been discovered that the chakras correlate to actual physiological processes. They act as transducers conducting energy in our body, stimulating hormone release and neurotransmission.

There is an appendix at the end of the book where you will find expanded content for each chapter. It is my hope that *Pony's Girl Parables* will be read contemplatively by adults, with curiosity by youth, and read to elementary school children. The appendix area is intended to spark conversation and self-reflection.

The chapter expansions include:

- A discussion about the archetype
- Summary of the chakra characteristics
- A meditation
- Pondering questions
- The back story behind the chapter

The audio version of the meditations can be found at this link: https://eponicity.com/ponys-girl-parables-audio-meditations/

Δ∇Δ∇Δ∇

Chapter 1

The Ambassador – Potential Unfolding

Life is not a pilgrimage to become an Ambassador, but rather a pilgrimage of remembering the Ambassador one was born to be.

This is the beginning; I will share three things to know right from the start.

1. The bee is Me, and I am the Bee.

2. We are all part of the One and one part of the All.

3. Remembering is only the beginning.

$$\Delta\nabla\Delta\nabla\Delta\nabla$$

I am busy buzzing amidst the big buds of clover in this bee body. I have obligations to my colony, and I like being a bee. Pony is enjoying the clover too, munching away on the violet delights. Here we go; today is to be a big day for Girl. She passes into her teen years, with this passage begins her remembering. Pony and I are here to join her now, in her pilgrimage to remembering the Ambassador she was born to be.

An Ambassador incorporates the vision of a Seer. A Seer sees unconditionally, collecting information in all forms and dimensions.

An Ambassador incorporates the ability of a Balancer to choose wisely. A Balancer lives by his noble truths and makes decisions based on what best serves the whole.

An Ambassador incorporates the awareness of a Sensor. A Sensor feels, senses, lives connected to the whole environment.

An Ambassador incorporates the capacity to collaborate of a Co-Creator. A Co-Creator aligns with himself and others to serve the unfolding potential.

An Ambassador incorporates the feelings of a Processor. A Processor has emotional resilience, using emotion as information for transformation.

An Ambassador incorporates the strength of a Protector. A Protector provides safety and security, ensuring the right to be.

An Ambassador leads with wisdom by incorporating all of these skills. During her pilgrimage, Girl will experience, practice and learn these skills, elements that are essential for any Ambassador.

△▽△▽△▽

"Mom, Dad, it's finally here; today, I am old enough for a pony!" It was her 13th birthday. Her parents agreed. They all hopped in the car and headed to Gerardo's ranch to pick out a pony for Girl.

"Which color horse would you like? I got all kinds out there," the rancher, Gerardo, used the pointy toe of his boot to direct their attention toward a variety of colorful equines. A dozen or so horses grazed in a big pasture dotted with violet clover, surrounded by dense forest.

"What color? Oh, I hadn't thought of that." Girl tapped her chin in contemplation. "What color is the most popular, Don Gerardo? I wonder what color my friends will think is really cool?"

"Well, it's up to you, dear." His eyes had a violet twinkle when he smiled. "It's a personal preference. Me, I like the spotted horses, appaloosas; they tickle my fancy!"

"What does that mean? 'Tickle my fancy?'" asked Girl.

"It's an old saying; it's a little tickle, like a smile in my belly, when I am around them. I like their looks, even more than that; appaloosas have a character that suits me. They are funny, tricky, and wise—together, we make a good team!" He opened the gate and waved them in, "Feel free to go out and mingle, see who 'tickles your fancy,' dear!"

3

Girl took the lead; her parents stayed a few paces behind her. She eyed a dark brown horse with a star on his forehead, a speckled grey mare with floppy ears, a chestnut pony with a wild mane and tail; she could *fancy* any of them! Then she saw him, and inside her heart, she felt a little tickle!

"That golden one. He is Pony, my pony. He tickles my fancy!" She skipped over to Pony, stopping politely before coming too close. "Is it ok to come closer, Pony? Can I pat your golden mane?" Instead, Pony moved toward her. She patted him and started talking to him; she was so excited, "...he is so wonderful, don't you just feel it, Dad, Mom?"

A bee (me) buzzed up from a patch of clover and started to buzz around them. Weighed down with pollen, I could only fly slowly, up and down around and around. Father tried to swish me away.

"Oh, Dad, a bee! I don't want Pony to get stung!" shouted Girl.

"Well, I don't want you to get stung either, dear, I'll smack it down and kill it." Father decided, since I did not take leave with the swooshing of his hand.

He raised his hand to swat me, but Pony, with a quick, intentional move, came between his hand and me. I landed safely on his forelock, and we trotted away to the edge of the forest. Then, Pony sent me into the forest with a toss of his head, and he trotted back to the family.

"Mother, did you just see that?" questioned Father.

"I don't know, did you, Father?" Mother rubbed her eyes, bewildered.

"I saw it, Dad! Pony saved us from the bee!" Girl exclaimed.

Pony, standing with the family, stared intently at Father, eyes not blinking; his body was totally still.

Father sensed there was more to understand and then understood, "Oh, Pony, I see. You didn't save us from the bee; you saved the bee from me!" Pony lowered his head, yawned, and sighed in agreement with Father's realization.

"Why would Pony do that? Do bees talk to horses? Do horses talk to bees? How did Pony know you wanted to smack the bee?" Girl too, was bewildered and curious.

"Dear, I think Pony reminded us to pay attention to Mother Nature," Mother explained and continued, "It is easy to think of the bee as just one little bee, but that bee is connected to his hive, his colony of bees, and honey. Bees pollinate plants and crops. We need the bees to do their work so we can have food to eat. It is not necessarily about killing that one little bee. Pony reminded us of how connected everything is."

"Thank you, Pony, for helping us remember; you are certainly a wise ambassador for Mother Earth!" Father declared in a stern fatherly voice.

At that moment, something shifted inside of Girl, as it was meant to. Things around her looked different, the trees, the grass, the horses, her parents, the rancher, the sky, the clouds; she felt connected to everything, and everything felt connected to her. "Pony is for me, and I am for him." Girl spoke with the wisdom of someone much older. The family stood quietly with Pony in the green pasture, surrounded by forest. A breeze fluttered through Pony's golden mane, the other horses nickered in the background; honey bees continued with their day, collecting nectar and pollen for their hive.

For a few moments, time was of no importance. When clouds moved in, it felt like it was time to go.

Father was the first to return to the task at hand. "Well, Pony, are you ready to join our family?"

Pony licked and chewed; this reply was a big "YES" in horse language!

Girl placed a violet-colored halter over Pony's golden head, "Happy birthday to me!" Girl cheered. Girl and Pony walked side by side out of the pasture.

Gerardo met them at the gate, "Well, I see you found a fellow that tickled your fancy."

"Yes, Don Gerardo, he sure does; I feel the tickle in my heart, thank you so much," replied Girl.

Since all eyes were on Pony as he hopped into the trailer, no one noticed me hiding in Pony's thick blond forelock! With a violet twinkle in his eye, Don Gerardo tipped his hat as the family drove off. Let the remembering begin!

Chapter 2

The Seer – See Unconditionally

Seeing everything unconditionally is an essential quality for an Ambassador.

Bees are great communicators. In the hive, we dance to deliver messages to our hive mates. What flowers are blooming, what direction, and how far away to fly are pieces of information that are communicated by our dance. When we see without condition, there is no judgment. Things are as they are. Data collected without judgment is fair, creating an authentic picture without discrimination. There is so much to see in this multidimensional world!

Today, purple lilacs are in bloom; their beautiful nectar-filled flowers are a favorite of bees. My prickly legs are picking up the next load of pollen as Girl comes skipping by me, headed for the barn. I leave the flowers to follow her and perch on an empty honey jar left on the window sill in Pony's stall.

Δ∇Δ∇Δ∇Δ∇

"Oooooh, Pony, where are youuuu...?" Girl called as she enters the barn. Since Pony came home with Girl, she spends every spare minute with him telling him all about what has been going on in her life.

Pony likes being in the limelight and enjoys Girl's adoration. In his younger days, he competed in rodeos and was often the center of attention. He felt good when people cheered for him! It was not winning that felt so good; it was the human connection and positive emotion that arose while he was racing around the barrels. "GO! GO! GO! FASTER! FASTER! FASTER!" The contagious cheers collided, creating an energetic wave of excitement.

Hearing Girl calling, Pony trotted back in from the barnyard. He had been checking on 12 new piglets, 20 baby chicks and warned one silly billy goat that eating an old can was not a good idea. He liked it here; everyone felt cared for and loved.

"There you are, you are such a busy body, Pony! Let's go back to your stall; I want to brush you and put ribbons in your mane." Pony did like ribbons for winning races, but not ribbons in his mane! He was a good sport, in any case, and stood quietly while Girl fussed over him.

"Today at school, my friend, Missy, was telling me about a fortune-teller she saw at the fair. She said the lady told her things that there was no way she could know. Like what color her room is painted, her cat's name, Mittens, and even that her grandmother died when she was 107 years old! How could she know that? She has ESP, I suppose—that stands for extrasensory perception, that is when you just know something that is not something you would logically know."

Girl's brow wrinkled, perplexed, "Sometimes I know things, maybe I have ESP. I get a funny feeling when it happens, it feels like glitter all over my body, and you know what, those things that I just 'knew,' well, they often come true! I wonder if everyone is born with ESP, like the fortune-teller, and we just forget how to 'know' things as we get older?"

She went on brushing and musing, "My dad says I'm too sensitive. Nowadays, I mostly try to ignore my feelings because sometimes they make me cry for no reason. My dad jokes and says, 'What are you crying about? I'll give you something to cry about.' Even though he's joking, it makes me feel bad." Girl became very quiet.

From my jar, I could see a single tear trickle down her cheek, "I feel the glitter less and less lately," she sniffed, "Oh, well, part of growing up, I suppose." She put down the brush and ribbons, pulled her canvas camping chair she called the "Pondering Chair" next to Pony and sat down. Leaning back in the chair, she began to think; she tapped her finger on her chin a few times. Her eyelids drifted down; her eyes closed. Pony, adorned with purple ribbons in his golden mane, lightly rested his soft muzzle on top of her head.

As they started to doze off, a warm spring breeze carried the sweet fragrance of the lilacs' purple blossoms through the barn and into the stall. The air thickened around them; it began to swirl. Pony and Girl, sensing a shift, opened their eyes to see the whirling air form a purple spiral.

"What is happening? Pony look! Am I dreaming?" Girl pinched herself hard and squealed. "Nope, I'm awake." The purple spiral became larger, widening, and its center opened, creating a passageway large enough for a pony to pass through. Time stood still; the purple passageway quietly waited.

"Pony, I don't know what is going on, but I have that glitter feeling all over my body! I seem to be able to 'hear' the passageway; it wants us to come in." My girl is very brave. Pony nudged Girl to hop on, and she did. He turned his head toward me; I flew down from the jar to my favorite spot in his forelock. Pony jumped into the swirling purple passageway. It was the portal to the In-Between.

△▽△▽△▽△▽

The In-Between is the space between the Solid World and the Merkabah World. The Solid World is where energy has taken form, shape, and purpose; it is Earth. The Merkabah World is the space that holds potential for what wants to happen and all that is possible.

While in the In-Between, parts of the All can be seen. The All is *everything from every fragment of time and space in the universe.* The In-Between holds our experiences of times before and to come, lessons learned and to be learned, Soul partners for this life and for all lives, signs from the past, and clues to the future. Everything in the In-Between is to be seen unconditionally.

△▽△▽△▽△▽

The In-Between carried us on purple rope-like waves of light. Pony's tail was straight up, flying like a golden flag as we rode the waves. The purple light shifted into countless vibrant colors; some colors do not have Earth names yet. The twisting, iridescent ropes of light released shapes, images, and memories: ladders, candy, books, appaloosas, owls, cowboys, shamans, witches, bones, tents, windy hills, boulders, babies, volcanoes, unicorns, soccer balls, feathers, statues, rabbits, cards, and many other images, too many to count. They all twisted and turned all around us as we rode through the In-Between.

After an immeasurable amount of time, we arrived at the other end of the passageway and entered the Merkabah World. We were at the end of a dirt road at the edge of a narrow, shallow river; swirls of water created eddies in nooks and crannies along the rocky shoreline. The river flowed out from a valley, then snaked around large boulders making its way down the mountain pass.

"Have I been here before? No, where are we? Am I dreaming?" Girl pinched herself again. "Ouch, nope, I'm awake." Girl was nervous, scared of the unknown; this was not like anything she'd ever experienced before.

"Should we pass through the river, Pony? I am getting a strong pulling and tingling feeling in my chest; it wants us to go into the valley." Girl wanted to trust the feeling. If she trusted it, she would be brave.

A few meters downstream, Pony spotted a secure way to enter and exit the river. The spot was shallow enough for him to cross without needing to swim, and the clear water was calm enough so he'd be able to see his hooves as he crossed. He did not like to swim or not be able to see his hooves. Girl, still on his back, saw what he saw, sensed his intention, and they headed to that spot to cross. Pony fixed his gaze on the exit spot at the other side of the river; he entered with power and determination and came out on the other side just fine. The water had only come up to the middle of his legs. Girl stayed dry, so I did I!

"Good job, Pony!" Girl rubbed his mane, hopped off his back, and kissed his cheek. "You kept me safe, thank you. I am still a bit nervous, not sure exactly where to go next."

A mossy trail crept up from the riverbank, summoning us toward the valley. An immense boulder shaped like a Volkswagen Bug stood as a sentinel guarding the entrance to the valley. Lichens growing on the boulder looked like big eyes watching us pass through a rusty barbwire gate and enter the valley. The trail followed the river; tall trees wrapped in peeling; rusty-red bark umbrellaed over the river's edge. Blue birds the size of chickens with curled, black feathers on the tops of their heads cawed down to us as they jumped from branch to branch. When enough time had passed for Girl to relax, the trail moved us away from the river into the forest. Sounds of the rushing water faded into peeping and chirping of the forest fauna.

The trail twisted around giant trees with shallow roots reaching out like gnarly fingers on the forest floor. Layers of sound, color, life, and light stacked from the ground, through the trees, and up to the sky, creating a complex, interdependent eco-system. A synchronistic world that communicates across every species, becoming one giant organism.

We came out of the forest into a valley protected by steep, grass- and scrub-covered hills, crowned by volcanic boulders and wind-blown cypress trees. A barren peak, the remains of an ancient volcano, guarded the far end of the valley. Wind raced across the top of the valley, chasing clouds from the west to the east, then back east to the west in an endless debate. The trail meandered through patches of forest, undergrowth, and wild grass.

Around a turn in the trail, a black and white striped owl swooped down and landed on a tree stump in front of us. A green parrot dropped down from someplace and perched next to the owl.

"Who, who are you looking for?" asked Owl. I could hear him; Pony could too; however, Girl couldn't understand him—*yet*.

Translating for Owl, Parrot repeated, in human language, "Who, who are you looking for?"

Girl turned to face the talking parrot. "I don't remember."

"Someone is expecting us," Pony said to Owl.

Parrot translated for Girl again. "Someone is expecting us."

"We are expected? Well, that is funny. I suppose my feelings are correct," Girl said out loud.

Owl and Parrot took flight. "I sense they want us to follow them," Girl said. So, we did.

The trail was interrupted by a big washout; climbing down and up the other side would be tricky. Owl, Parrot, and I flew across; it is nice to have wings! Pony slid down the steep, earthen bank and waited for Girl at the bottom. She sat and slid down the muddy slope, landing right under Pony. He stood as still as a statue, waiting. Laughing, covered with mud, she scooted out from under his belly and got up.

"Ok, Pony, you can help me, you climb up little by little, and I'll hold your tail like a rope to pull myself up." That was his plan, too; she was beginning to remember how to communicate without words. He started up the slope, digging his

16

hooves into the side of the slippery ravine to gain solid footing. He held firm and steady for Girl as she grabbed his tail and hoisted herself up to his level. They continued the assent step-by-step until reaching the top of the embankment.

Excellent teamwork, thought Pony.

"Excellent teamwork!" echoed Girl.

"Excellent teamwork!" repeated Parrot.

The gradually sloping trail led back down to the riverbank; it ended at a waterfall. The falling water spilled into an eye-shaped pool encircled by smooth rocks. Ferns grew between the stones; they fluttered like eyelashes in the turbulent, misty air. Girl sat on one of the flat stones. A butterfly, as large as her father's hand and as blue as his eyes, glided above the pond.

"I'm tired and thirsty; that was quite a hike. I feel like I know this place, but I don't know where I am or how I got here." She picked up a pebble and threw it into the center of the pond.

Moss and miniature fern-like plants covered the wide rock wall on either side of the waterfall; water seeped through the vertical green blanket. Pony walked over to the wall, looked back at Girl, and licked water trickling from the wall; she joined him and collected water in cupped hands. She splashed the cool water on her muddy face and drank the naturally filtered water.

"So sweet, so pure, this water must come right from heaven!" She smiled.

A thin green vine came out of the misty air and brushed against her bare arm. It wrapped itself three times around her wrist, but it was not a vine; it was a thin green snake. Girl instinctually remained calm on the outside; however, on the inside, she was startled! Last winter, she had written a report on snakes but had never had a close encounter with a snake. She remembered what she had learned and, upon studying this snake, discerned it was a non-venomous vine snake. A good omen, she thought. She felt called to look up; Owl and Parrot were looking down at her. She heard Parrot say, "A gift from the forest, Girl."

"Why, thank you, Parrot!" She smiled at the winged duo.

Pony had gone over to the edge of the pool; he needed a big drink; licking the weeping wall wasn't enough to quench his thirst. He heard a noise, raised his head; a brown appaloosa with white spots came out of the mist. The horse walked over to Girl and stood directly in front of her.

"Well, hello there," said Girl. The horse snorted through his nose and pawed at the ground in response to her greeting. Parrot swooped down and landed on the horse's head right between his ears.

"He wants me to translate for him," said Parrot. "Don't worry, he can understand you."

"Ok, nice to meet you. Do you know why I am here?" Girl questioned him.

"Yes, I do; I called for you, Girl," said Parrot, speaking for the horse. "This is your Valley of Signs and Wonders. I welcome you; I am Cosmos. The Valley of Signs and Wonders holds your lifetimes of memories. Come to this place anytime, to remember," he suggested.

"No wonder it feels familiar, and I am not afraid, only a bit confused. What do you mean about lifetimes?" Girl asked.

He continued, "Mist arising from the waterfall holds all of the memories of the river. The mist, now separate from the river, is on a journey. Eventually, it evaporates into the air, becomes part of a cloud, then becomes rain, returning to the river bringing the richness it has gathered during its journey. Through all of its transformations, it never forgets it is water." Cosmos shook his head, then nodded. "Dear, remember you are not one drop of the river, but the whole river in one drop. This valley is your river."

After a few moments of silence, Cosmos spoke, "I am to tell you a story, a story you will remember in the years to come. It is important to remember, remembering it will bring you back to this place, and you will know you are on the right path."

$$\Delta \nabla \Delta \nabla \Delta \nabla \Delta \nabla$$

He began -

A stocky rancher at a weekly livestock auction walks down rows of holding pens filled with cattle and horses, a sickly-looking appaloosa destined for the meat processing plant, catches his eye, the horse's condemned eye catches him as well.

He places offers on some cattle but doesn't win any of the bids; however, he couldn't lose the feeling of doom in the eyes of the horse whose gaze had haunted him the whole afternoon.

When the auction ended, he climbed into his empty truck to head home, but he couldn't shake the feeling of doom; it didn't make any sense to him. Every week at the auction, he

19

passed by countless, useless horses; why was the eye of this old nag still haunting him? Conceding to the feeling, he doubled back, pulled up next to the cattle truck transporting the horse to the meat processing plant and gave the man the meat price for the horse. He hopped in the back, tied a rope around the horse's skinny neck, squeezed him through the cargo of wide-eyed cattle, and loaded him onto his truck. Now it was time to go home.

The horse was bones and skin; the scars on his head, face, and body and lumps on his swayed back were living evidence of a difficult life. Through the village grapevine, he discovered that the horse had been owned by a mean drunkard, who used the horse to slip into farms at night and steal cattle.

Over the next six months, he nursed the horse back to health. With good nutrition and a loving hand, the horse's dull, muddy brown coat transformed to a shiny dark chocolate brown, the white spots on the appaloosa's rump reminded the rancher of stars in the night sky. The grateful horse was an excellent partner for the rancher, devoted, hardworking, and well-skilled.

A year passed, then one day, the rancher and horse were working with a herd of mature, 2,000-pound long-horn bulls. They were maneuvering the bulls into a small corral, preparing for a truck transport. Without warning, an angry bull charged the rancher; his chest was the obvious target of the three-foot-long horn.

The agile and quick-witted horse deliberately reared up to block the attack aimed to kill the rancher. The horn missed its mark and instead pierced the horse's soft belly. Fatally wounded, the horse looked back at his Soul mate. Again, at death's door, they were eye-to-eye. But, this time, the rancher saw not doom in the equine's eye but gratitude. As he fell, the horse carefully positioned his body to shield the man from the angry bulls, leaving just enough room for him to roll under the fence to safety, valiantly saving his savior.

A month later, the rancher was at a village party. A friend of his son was expected to be at the party; he wanted to talk to her, there was a rumor she could communicate with horses. He wanted to ask her a question.

The woman came galloping up the dirt road on a big, black mare, her wild, white hair flying parallel to the horse's black tail. He met her as she came to a stop and held the horse for her as she dismounted. They shared polite conversation for a few minutes. Then, when it was time, he told her the story of his horse. She listened intently to his tale.

When the story finished, then came the rancher's question, "Ma'am, they say you know how horses think; why, why did that critter sacrifice himself for me?"

"Don Gerardo, because you listened, you saved him first." Her blue eyes twinkled behind her tears.

The woman's magnificent mare yawned and blew through her lips; Gerardo's eyes met her dark, endless gaze; he heard, "Everything is connected."

The rancher's eyes filled with tears; each tear connected him to everything he knew.

As Cosmos finished the story, he lowered his head, and Parrot flew up to a nearby branch now silent.

Girl started to cry, her tears filled with benevolence, awe, and miracles. Pony gently rubbed circles on the top of her head with his soft muzzle. "Will that be part of my story, Cosmos?" Girl sniffled.

"Yes, your guides will communicate to you through others, through animals, ómens, and by 'knowings' when you meditate, or as you say, 'ponder.' Follow the signs; they are your waypoints and guideposts to your remembering, dear." Cosmos turned and started up the trail. "Follow me."

Single file, two horses, a parrot, an owl, a girl with a snake bracelet, and me, the bee, moved through the forest and into a circular clearing at the base of the old volcano.

It was getting dark. The wind continued to blow above the valley, shaping moonlit clouds in the night sky. Above the old volcano, a smooth cap of clouds was spinning slowly on top of its peak.

Cosmos looked up at Owl and nodded. Owl started flying in circles in the air, opening the purple passageway. Girl, too, sensed it was time. As she hopped on Pony's back, the green vine snake transformed into silver, the eyes of the snake morphed into purple crystals. She touched it to be sure; yes, it was solid, it was real. She nodded to Cosmos, Parrot, and Owl, and the three of us entered the welcoming swirl.

Δ∇Δ∇Δ∇

We moved through the In-between quickly and landed right where we started. I on top of the empty honey jar, Girl in the Pondering Chair with Pony at her side.

"What just happened?" Girl looked around the stall in wonder. "What happened couldn't have really happened. It must have all been a dream." A ray of sunlight sparked the purple crystal eyes of the silver snake, validating the experience. She touched the bracelet and felt a tingle between her pale blue

23

eyes. In a bit of a daze, she shook her head and silently went into the house.

"Hi, dear!" Mother greeted her, handing her an envelope, "Surprise! We booked the family vacation!"

Girl opened the envelope and pulled out a travel brochure. On the cover was a cloud-capped volcano; at the base of the volcano stood a brown appaloosa with white spots.

Chapter 3

The Balancer – Choose Truth

The Balancer removes what is no longer serving the whole to make room for what wants to happen next, an essential attribute of an Ambassador.

Girl has celebrated three more birthdays. Braids, threaded with colorful feathers, have replaced the frilly ribbons in Pony's mane. The Pondering Chair has been well used; she has spent many hours there, moving through the In-Between to the Valley of Signs and Wonders. Girl is remembering more and more. Bees live a much shorter time. I've changed bee bodies countless times during this Ambassadorship for Girl.

Girl faces a choice. She and her friend have planned for months to participate in *The Walk for Mankind* on Saturday. It's a 20-mile walk to raise funds for local charities. I see Girl and Mother in the kitchen from my sweet spot on the hummingbird (and bee) feeder.

"Mom, I have a dilemma," Girl began dramatically, as 16-year-olds often do.

"Yes, dear, tell me about it." Mother didn't bother turning away from the pressure cooker she was loading with jars of cucumbers destined to become dill pickles.

"You know Sue and I had planned on participating in *The Walk for Mankind* event on Saturday, but I may want to change my mind. My other friend, Lori, is having a birthday party at the river, and everyone is going tubing. It sounds like so much fun, and besides, how can I tell her I have other plans that are more important than her party?"

Mother glanced out the window, looking my way, for a hummingbird, I suppose, then turned to Girl. "Now dear, haven't you been collecting pledges for that walk for the last few months?"

"Yes, but no one pays until I actually log the miles. So, it's no big deal, right?"

"Well, just a minute, let's think about the choice you have before you," Mother replied to Girl's attempt at rationalization.

"Oh, no, don't say, '*What would Jesus or Buddha or Gandhi or Mother Theresa do,*' I am a teenager, not a saint!" Girl knew all too well where this conversation was going.

"Ok, I won't." Mother turned around and let Girl be in her pickle while she went back to making pickles.

"I'm going out to the barn; I'll see you later." I sensed her whisper, '*Buddha*' under her breath as she headed out the door.

I got one last sip from the hummingbird feeder and buzzed along behind Girl. She plopped down in the Pondering Chair next to Pony, who was munching on hay.

Δ∇Δ∇Δ∇Δ∇

"Pony, I'm in a pickle. I need to figure it out." She leaned back in her chair, closed her eyes, and began to go to her place to ponder, accompanied by the sound of Pony chewing. Her quiet breath—*out and in, out and in*—opened the portal to the In-Between. A blue spiraling passageway appeared, and away we went.

We passed through the In-Between, riding on ropey shades of blue. A bright white Buddha waved as we passed by, nuns in black and white robes blew us kisses, Gandhi smiled and nodded; Jesus waved us out of the passageway and onto the damp stone floor of a cave.

Girl and Pony needed a few minutes to adjust to the dim light in the Merkabah World cave. I could see just fine, as bees have excellent vision! The room was as large as the barn and tall as a house. A beam of sunshine flowed through a hole in the ceiling; it fell onto a still, silvery pond in the center of the cave.

Light coming from the cave entrance provided additional illumination. Hundreds of rainbow-colored stalactites hung from the ceiling, rhythmically offering mineral water to their partnering stalagmite. Each growing drop by drop, in constant transformation, one day they would touch and become one vertical column adding strength to the entire cave.

Girl explored the wonderous room of the cave, eventually squatting down at the edge of the pond; she peered into the water. "Look, I can see my reflection." Pony walked over next to her and saw his reflection too; he snorted. "Silly pony, it's you!" Girl laughed. "I'm ready for this adventure, Pony; are you?" She scratched his neck and threw a tiny stone into the pond, and they watched the rings carry their reflection away. I flew down, grabbed Pony's forelock, and we headed off toward the light.

The entrance to the cave was shaped like the wide mouth of a frog; dark green moss carpeted the entrance, a welcome mat to the world above ground. A rocky trail led us to an ancient forest with trees a hundred feet tall reaching toward the light. Inside the forest, countless years of pine needles softened the rocky path. We came to a choice; the path was split in two by a large boulder.

Girl tapped the space between her eyes; it was tingling. "Which way should we go, right or left?"

A voice came from behind the boulder answering her question with a question, "Would you like to choose the noble path or the easy path?" A tall, lean man, dressed in a bluish-white robe; his head wrapped in a blue turban, appeared from the forest. He jumped up on the boulder and raised his arms out to his sides, pointing in both directions—"Noble to the right or easy to the left?"

"I choose noble, of course, But if it is not easy, is it hard?" Girl looked puzzled. Pony and I were not confused; there really is no choice.

"Until you know your truth, it can be a confusing choice. I am Satya; I will be your guide." Satya whistled softly; a blue-roan horse trotted up the path toward us. Pony and the blue-roan arched their necks up, ears pointing forward; they touched muzzles in a familiar greeting.

"This is my friend, Stella," he said, introducing his horse companion. "Let's follow the noble path then; are you ready for an adventure, dear ones?" Girl, Pony, and Stella all nodded in unison; we were off, to the right.

$$\Delta\nabla\Delta\nabla\Delta\nabla\Delta\nabla$$

Open spaces in the canopy let in light. Butterflies, dragonflies, and bees collected nectar, pollinating the flowers that grew in the sun-lit areas on the forest floor. A large branch covered with curly black fungi and mosses arched over the path at a turn in the trail.

"Look closely at the branch, dear; what do you see?" questioned Satya.

"I see many interesting plants growing within the nooks and crannies of the tree's bark. It is like a miniature world. Oh, and I see cocoons." Eight white cocoons hung under the branch, tethered to the rough bark. "Look, one is emerging!" she added.

"Yes, what was once a caterpillar will soon take his first flight as a butterfly. The caterpillar does not know why he is compelled to create his cocoon. Once inside the cocoon, his body resists the change that will happen; if there is pain, it is inevitable; however, he suffers only in his resistance. Eventually, his caterpillar body is deconstructed; all that is left is his essence. This essence is what he takes with him; all else will not serve him as a butterfly. The cocoon may have seemed like his coffin, but in the end, it was his castle of transformation." Satya winked at Girl.

Girl, tapped her chin, thinking about this, "Why does he have to suffer?"

"We cannot escape pain, dear, but we can choose not to suffer. Pain is part of our existence. A lobster begins to feel the pain from the pressure of his old shell; this pain prompts him to shed his old shell and grow a new one. The pain of the pressure of the old shell is an indication that it is time to grow. A mother soon forgets the pain of childbirth; she lets go of the pain; motherly love overtakes the suffering that may be in the shadows."

Girl listened intently while keeping her eye on the emerging butterfly.

"Sometimes, when painful things happen, it indicates that something new wants to happen. That means it's time to release what we have outgrown to create space for something new to unfold. The pain lets us know it's time to become a bigger lobster!" Pony nudged the ground a bit with his muzzle, uncovering a fat green caterpillar.

Satya continued, with a cautionary tone, "The greatest triumph along our journey is to transform our pain into wisdom. The greatest wickedness is to intentionally cause others to suffer."

Stella was standing behind Girl; she could sense her breath on the back of her neck. Then the butterfly emerged. Little by little, its blue wings unfolded into a stream of sunlight and became iridescence as they dried. She practiced opening and closing her wings while still clinging to the cocoon.

"When the time is right, she will let go of the cocoon, and all that was before will be released, free to be what she is now at this moment, a butterfly, and she will not apologize for her time as a caterpillar, it was part of her journey." Satya took a step back, as did Stella, and the butterfly took flight.

"Dear, what truth do you know from this experience?" he asked.

"Pain is inevitable; it is a natural process; suffering is optional." Girl sighed; she had a knowing now.

"A noble truth, dear," Satya acknowledged. "Let's move on."

Butterflies and dragonflies created movement in between the majesty of trees. Stella was in the lead, then Pony and I, Girl and Satya trailing behind. Stella stopped suddenly, glanced guardedly back at Satya. Taking her cue, he went up ahead to inspect. In a moment, he came back and silently motioned us to proceed. The path led to a clearing along the bank of a broad, quiet river. Lying on the sunny, sandy shore, a 10-foot-long crocodile was warming himself. His mouth was wide open. Inside his mouth, a speckled bird was calmly pecking at his teeth.

Girl's eyes were wide; she whispered, "Oh, my, that bird better get out of there before it gets eaten!"

"I think the croc is full; he's had his share for the day." Satya smiled. "It's a lovely sight; look again, dear, what do you notice?"

"Why doesn't he just eat the bird? I am sure he can fit another mouthful in that big belly!" Girl was standing in cover behind Satya, peeking around him at the unlikely duo on the river bank.

"He is not hateful; the bird is doing him a favor; she is cleaning his teeth, making a meal of the leftovers stuck between them." Satya went on, "Nature is not hateful, even a predator like the crocodile loves over hate; on the contrary, he and the bird have a symbiotic relationship."

"From the outside, I see a foolish bird in the mouth of a scary crocodile. But, now that I have more information, I know the truth." Girl was starting to understand about nobility.

"Hate does not have a place in nature. Nature relies on symbiotic relationships to thrive." Satya added. "When you first saw the pair, you judged the crocodile; after you had more information, what changed?"

"My judgment changed to more like an assessment of the situation; I was curious to understand and know more about what was actually going on."

"Tell me another noble truth, dear."

"Be curious, not judgmental, and the truth can be seen," realized Girl.

The bird finished her job; she was preening her feathers, still in the crocodile's open mouth. The croc grunted; she took the cue, hopped out of his mouth and onto the top of his head. Gently he closed his mouth. They both closed their eyes; it was time for a nap.

We continued on the path; it ended at the bank of a smaller river that eventually spilled into the larger one, the home of the crocodile and the bird.

"We have to cross here. The water is deep, dear. It would be best for us to ride the horses through," Satya advised. Girl took a step back; Pony felt her hesitation and looked at Stella.

"Pony does not like water, Satya. He is afraid." Girl was sure he would not do it. She didn't think it was a good idea either. What if they sank? After all, there are crocodiles in the water, and who knows what else! Pony sensed her nervousness that made him nervous, too; nervous energy is contagious.

"So, what do we do then? What are our choices?" asked Satya.

"Well, we can go back," Girl said.

"What are the consequences of that choice?" he questioned.

"We will be safe, but we would not know what is on the other side of the river." Girl mused, "Or we could find another route that is easier."

"Oh, so you would like to find an easier way?" Satya said, "What are the consequences of that choice?"

"Pony wouldn't learn to swim or get over his fear of water. The man at the place where he used to live said he didn't like water; he had a bad experience in the past," Girl explained.

"Do you think he is capable of learning to swim?" asked Satya.

"Yes, of course, he's a horse!" replied Girl, with a hint of optimism in her voice.

"So, now we have clarity around the real choice. One— choose to keep Pony as a victim of that old story, or two—support him in transforming the story into something useful." Satya was an excellent guide; he was encouraging Girl to think about the responsibility that comes with choice.

The river flowed slowly past them as Girl thought about the choices in front of her. Pony was brave; if she didn't believe in him, he would never believe in himself. Partners make the best of each other.

"I want to choose to cross, Satya, but I don't know how we can do it."

"You've come to another choice. What are your choices?" Satya knew his student was making progress and smiled at Stella.

"Well, I suppose it comes down to two choices, we can do it ourselves, or we can ask for help. I choose help. Can you help us, Satya?"

"I thought you would never ask! Yes, of course, Stella and I have done this many times. Pay attention, child. Come and stand by me; let go and let Stella start the new story for Pony. Horses are the best teachers for other horses!"

Stella touched Pony on the nose, then on the shoulder, then on the withers. They walked down to the very edge of the river. The water was tapping Pony's hooves, he stood still and watched Stella enter the river. Keeping her eyes fixed on a spot on the other side, she calmly swam across and climbed out of the river right at that spot. Stella whinnied to Pony. She did not doubt he could make it. Pony whinnied back to her, and he went in.

I stayed on Pony's forehead, just for fun, and held on tight to his forelock. I had confidence in him. With his eyes on Stella, he swam with ease to the other side and proudly trotted up the bank to stand next to her. He made a big snort and whinnied back at Girl. I flew off to a branch to watch what happened next.

Girl started clapping and jumping up and down. "Yay, yay for Pony! Good job!"

"Hey, what about us! Don't leave us here; we need your help!" Satya pretended to plead with the horses. Stella and Pony snorted and jumped back in the river together, swimming across like a pair of fish. They climbed up the riverbank and shook off the water, giving Girl and Satya a nice shower.

Girl was nervous but excited. "Satya, how do I hold on?"

"I will show you." He gave her a boost up onto Pony. "Lean forward, hold around his neck, let your legs flow behind you, like this." He helped her get into the position, practicing on the land. "Look where he is looking, trust him. Trust is the secret to bravery, dear."

"Stella and I will go in just after the two of you; we'll be right behind you. Your guides always have your back, remember that," Satya assured her.

Pony stepped with care to the water's edge, looked back at Girl. She was ready. They set their sights on a spot on the opposite side. He entered the river; the shore gave way to the water, and he began to swim. Girl hung on to Pony's neck; her body flowed over his back; her legs trailed behind. She felt like a part of his powerful body as it pushed effortlessly through the water. The river was not the obstacle; the real obstacle was the old story.

Stella carried Satya across with ease, as they, too, were one heart.

"Good job, everyone!" Satya was delighted.

"Yes, that was great, Satya, it was even fun! I am so happy I was brave; I mean, WE were brave, right Pony?!" she exclaimed.

Satya nodded and smiled, "Girl, what is your noble truth?"

"Let me see...well, choosing to let go of something that held us back helped us grow, it's a good idea to think things through before I choose too quickly, and it's ok to ask for help. *My truth is to release what does not serve me*—and things will fall into place as they should." Girl was becoming wise already.

"Very good, dear. You are a good student." Satya was pleased with her progress.

Girl and Satya dismounted, we all headed down the path again. I collected a few *nectar-licious* snacks along the way. Then we were back at the boulder, where we started.

Girl was surprised, "How did we end up back here?"

"You've learned your truths already, dear."

"I did? That seemed pretty easy. Can noble be easy, Satya?"

Satya, the great teacher, smiled and nodded. "Yes, the easiest solution to any predicament is to choose truth. The noble choice is the choice that restores balance." He handed Girl a thick paper scroll tied with a thin braid of blue-roan horsehair. "Here, dear, this is for you."

Girl carefully untied the scroll and unrolled it. It read:

Truth is Balance ~ Balance is Truth

Pain is inevitable; it is a natural process, suffering is optional.

Be curious, not judgmental, and the truth can be seen.

Release what does not serve you.

Choose Truth

Girl rolled the scroll and retied it with the cord made from Stella's tail hair. When she looked up, she noticed the trail to the left had vanished; there was only one option now, the noble path. Satya nodded as if he had read her thoughts.

A blue hue began to form around the big boulder at the trailhead. It was time to leave this Merkabah World. Girl hugged Satya and Stella. Pony nickered at Stella; I situated myself in his thick forelock. Girl hopped on Pony's back with her truths in hand and heart. When the passageway opened, Pony jumped in bravely and nobly.

In the Solid World, Girl found herself in the Pondering Chair with the scroll still in her hand and sighed. "I know now; I have only one choice for Saturday, don't I Pony?" He snorted and yawned with a violet twinkle in his eye. Girl too was noble and brave and an asset to mankind.

Chapter 4

The Sensor – Live Connected

The Sensor appreciates Earth as one whole, living organism, an essential quality for an Ambassador.

The fields around Girl's house are green, green, green! As far as a bee can see. Country roads crisscross the fields; the country roads connect to highways, and the highways connect to the interstates that brought the family together today. It is a gathering to celebrate Grandmother's 100th birthday. I will observe the festivities from the cornfield; corn pollen makes an interesting type of honey.

"Grandma, tell us a story of the olden days!" asked Girl's cousin. The family was sitting under an ancient black walnut tree, on the grass, on lawn chairs, or at a rickety old picnic table eating watermelon. Juicy, smiling faces all nodded in agreement.

"Ok, dears, let me think... well, I will tell you about the time I rode a camel in Egypt. It was back in the olden days when I was just 84 years old!" Grandmother laughed at her joke and continued, "It had always been a dream of mine to go to Egypt and ride a camel! I grew up riding horses, I love horses, so I thought I'd like to try a camel before I got too old." She winked, everyone laughed.

"I took in the sights, sounds, and smells of the country. It all felt very unfamiliar to me at first; it started to feel less unusual after a few days. My tour group was a bunch of tough and curious old ladies; it was a good group. Sadly, I am the only one still living," she added solemnly. "Anyway, where was I? Oh yes, the day finally came for us to ride the camels; most of the other ladies opted out, but not me; it was the day I was looking forward to the most! The camel knelt on the sand, and a nice man helped me to get on. He told me to hold on tight while the camel stood up; actually, it was very smooth; I was surprised. The man led me around for a few minutes while I got my balance and learned to steer the creature. When I was ready to try on my own, he let me go but kept a close eye on me. Well, don't you know, there I was, an old woman in her 80s plodding around in the sand below the pyramids in Egypt! Wow, what a feeling that was."

Grandmother smiled, remembering, "You know what, when I was on that camel, all I could think about was my beloved horse growing up, her name was Stella, she was a beautiful blue-roan colored horse; we were together for most of my childhood. When it was time for me to get off the camel, I asked the man what my camel's name was, he said it was Stella! Imagine that!" She smiled again. "What a coincidence!"

All the family gasped at once. It was a good story reminding me how we experience the Merkabah World in the Solid World. Coincidences, synchronicities are never random. Girl is learning to pay attention to them; they are gifts from the All.

"Hey, let's go and play kick the can, everyone!" Girl hollered at her cousins. "Meet you all at the old cemetery in 15 minutes." Girl and her cousin, Howard, went on ahead. He carried an old paint can to use in the game.

I flew along behind to watch the fun. Sun-shadows were giving way to the shadows of the full moon, a perfect night for playing. Kick the can was a generational family tradition. It is a hide-and-seek type of game, the person who is "it" uses all their senses to scan the environment to stay one step ahead of the rest of the players. They have to "capture" all of the other players by spotting them, running back to the can, and declaring their hiding spot. If someone beats them back to the can and kicks it, everyone goes free, and the capturing starts all over again. The game went on long into the night; I flew back to my hive before a winner was declared; bees don't stay up late.

The following day, I was collecting nectar from the pink roses around the patio. Girl, her parents, and grandmother were sitting outside having breakfast.

"We had such a great time last night, playing kick the can!" Girl said to her grandmother. "I was 'it' for a long time. I finally caught everyone by being very quiet and listening to everything around me and sensed where the others were hiding; then, I just called out their names and where they were. I didn't even move my foot off the can!"

"Wow, you're a good sensor, dear," Mother congratulated her.

"I remember playing that way too; just by sensing and using my intuition, I could connect to the information, I let it speak to me," Grandmother recalled.

"Well, now that everyone has gone off, I'd better do my chores and see what Pony is up to, later girls." Girl smiled and trotted off to the barn.

She noticed cobwebs in the corners and eves of the barn and grabbed a long-handled broom and started to sweep them down. One thing led to another, and she spent the next few hours cleaning and organizing. The barn hadn't been this clean for a long time! Luckily, she didn't clean up my sticky old honey jar.

Eventually, she finished and sat down in her Pondering Chair. Pony nudged her hand, indicating he wanted her to scratch an itch under his chin. Scratching his itch, she closed her eyes and wondered what more there was to know about this universal connection. After a few moments of breathing— *out and in, out and in*—there was a whirring sound; she opened her eyes to see a portal open; a slowly swirling pink and green passageway.

"Here we go, Pony. Perfect timing too!" I managed to cling to Pony's forelock just before he made the jump.

$$\triangle\triangledown\triangle\triangledown\triangle\triangledown$$

The In-Between world was layered with waves of pink and green. The pink waves gave momentum to the green waves. The waves of energy were embedded with fine translucent filament-like strands; the strands moved in harmony with us. Pony cantered over the smooth-rolling waves onto a tropical beach with powdered sugar sand. Girl kicked off her shoes and hopped off Pony; he wanted to roll in the soft, velvety, warm sand. Supported by the warm tropical air currents, I flew up to get a bird's-eye view of this Merkabah World.

Waves rhythmically moistened the white sand and black lava rocks that lined the shore. A pod of humpback whales swam in the sky-blue bay, coming up for air, one by one, composing a saltwater symphony of vertical exhale and inhale. The ocean rolled smoothly, its glassy surface rippling at times, when hundreds of silvery fish surfaced to nibble on tiny creatures clinging to floating seaweed. Pelicans glided low, frigate birds soared high, lifted by the breath of the ocean.

The jungle grew to the sea, the sliver of beach, a pause between the beat of the two eco-systems. The jungle's diversity of trees were painted 50 shades of green; branches offered a place for air plants, fungi, and mosses to take hold. Colorful birds checked the plants for insects and fresh water in the reservoirs created by their cuplike leaves. White-faced monkeys napped in the shaded branches. My bee senses appreciated how beautifully the pulse of the ocean harmonized with the beat of the jungle, in concert with the sky above and the land below.

Pony's hooves sunk in the sand next to Girl's bare footprints as they walked along the beach. Girl decided to run up ahead; when she was about 100 yards in front of Pony, she turned and faced him.

"Run, Pony, run. GO! GO! GO!" She loved to see him run, and he couldn't resist the cheering! He ran right on past Girl with his tail straight up, a golden flag flying in the wind. The beat of his hoofs added to the harmony of the surrounding symphony. When he won his imaginary race, he pranced around, head held high and his tail still perked up like a winner's flag. "And coming in first place is PONY, the winner by a mile!" announced Girl.

"Well, I don't know about that! He was the only one in the race!" shouted an incoming voice from behind her. Girl turned around. The voice came from a thin man wearing shorts, a white t-shirt, and a big pink and green knit hat. He was riding a creamy-white horse with a golden mane and tail; however, this was not just a horse; it was a unicorn!

Thump-thump-de-dump, thump-thump-de-dump beat its hooves as they trotted up to them. The unicorn stopped in front of Pony and Girl; the unicorn was twice Pony's size. They arched their necks and touched noses in a friendly greeting. The man hopped off; his big bare feet sunk into the sand. He began to dance and sing. The unicorn trotted around him; he swayed in rhythm to the song.

"Live connected, love connected

This is the way we are protected

Live connected, love connected

In this way, our bonds are cemented."

"Hello, sir, dancing with a unicorn!" greeted Girl.

He blew a kiss towards the unicorn's rainbow, spiraled horn. "Yes, Beauty and I have been together, always, our hearts beat as one. We are one love, one heart."

"Girl, and I are one heart, too." Girl heard Pony say.

"Pony, I heard you; I understood what you said, but how could I? You cannot speak?"

"Here, we are tapped into Earth's universal field. This vibration is the communication field that is everywhere and connects all of life." Explained the man. "I am Enrique; this is my Beauty," nodding at the unicorn.

"Let's go for a ride, Girl." Beauty said as she bowed down into the sand, "Grab hold of my horn, swing up on my back, and hold on to my mane. Live connected; love connected." The unicorn could sing too! Tears welled up in Girl's eyes; Beauty's invitation was the song of her dreams.

"Go, Girl, run Girl! GO! GO! GO!" Now Pony was cheering for her.

They ran down the beach; monkeys chattered, "It's too hot to run, unicorn, take a nap!"

Enrique, Pony, and I found some shade under a coconut palm. Enrique took a seat and leaned back against the tree. Pony dropped to the ground, "Hey, Bee, I'm going to roll in the sand!" Pony warned. I flew off to look for some nectar and join the pulse of the jungle.

Beauty turned into the sea; Girl held on tightly as the sand gave way under the unicorn's hooves. Soon they were swimming, moving up and down with the ocean swells.

A dolphin swam up alongside them, "Hello, human girl, nice day, isn't it?!"

Girl made a squealing dolphin-like sound. She was joyously laughing, swimming with a unicorn, talking to dolphins in the rolling sea; it was the best day ever!

A whale surfaced for a breath—out and in—his eye spoke to her, "Watch this human girl!" He swam a *seemingly* safe distance away from them and breeched high up in the air; the big splash created a wave that knocked Girl off of Beauty! Her head quickly popped up out of the water; she was just fine.

The dolphin came up under her. "Hang on, I'll take you back to the unicorn!" said the dolphin. He matched the speed of the swimming unicorn, making it easy for Girl to get back on. Celebrating the safe reunion, the dolphin jumped into the air and hollered, "See ya later!" They returned to the beach exhilarated.

"Enrique, I feel so connected, connected to everything. The animals, the ocean, the sky, the jungle...just everything...there is so much going on all around us, I can feel the pulse of it, like one giant beating heart. I do not think there is a word for it in English!"

Still sitting cross-legged under the coconut tree, the sun reflected a violet sparkle of light from Enrique's ageless eyes.

"Girl, connected heart, in Spanish there is a word 'vinculo.' Vinculo defines an unexplainable bond. Dear, you can use the vinculo that you feel to gather layers of information to be a Sensor of the whole truth. Close your eyes, breathe in, breathe out... breathe with your heart."

Pony then took over and guided her into this unseen world, "Close your eyes, feel the pulse around you. Listen with your heart. Sense with your heart. Notice, sense everything," Pony directed. "Now, dear, let your breath connect you to the ground...to the sky...to the jungle...the ocean, join the waves of energy that connect it to All."

Girl stood quietly with her eyes closed, toes held by the sand, sun shining on her wet hair, the breeze caressing her skin, waves lapping at her ankles, earthy scents floated out of the jungle, all inviting her to notice her musical signature in nature's symphony.

Some time passed, enveloped in all that surrounded her; finally, she spoke, "I am part of the All, the All is inside of me. I can sense everything as a connected part of everything else and Earth as one big living, pulsing organism created from all of the connected parts."

"Now, just for a moment, Girl, open your eyes and visualize the world as if nothing was connected," Enrique directed.

Girl opened her eyes and imagined that everything was separate. Although it touched the sandy beach, the ocean was not connected to it, the whale living in the sea was not a part of it, the birds in the jungle, although living in the trees, were solitary, and Pony was just a pony. Her breath caught in her throat; her heart started to race like she was lost; she wanted to cry. Enrique sensed her reaction.

"Ok, go back to the place of connection." Girl, with eyes open, re-connected everything in sight and out of sight. Her heart settled down, and she felt at peace again. "What do you understand?" asked Enrique.

"Everything is connected, or nothing is connected." Something in her shifted with this awareness. The horse and the unicorn nodded in unison. Once you know something for sure, a truth, you cannot un-know it. Life changes after that.

They all were quiet for a time. Waves moistened the sand, sealing its connection. Seagulls soared, connected to the air. Hermit crabs dug holes in the sand connected to the earth. Girl breathed in and out; her breath connected her to the All.

Beauty dipped her horn into the sand and pulled up an iridescent pink and green seashell. "Here, this is for you, dear." Girl put it in her zippered pants pocket for safekeeping.

The sun was touching the ocean now; there was a change to the pulse in the fading light. A pinkish green swirl of light appeared next to the coconut palm. It was time to go.

Girl hugged Enrique and Beauty. Humming their tune—*live connected, love connected*—she hopped on Pony's back, we jumped into the In-Between. Pink and green ropes of energetic waves remained tethered to the Merkabah world as we passed back into the Solid World. Girl's connection to her remembering was getting stronger.

Chapter 5

The Co-Creator – Two Aligned Are More Than the Sum

The Co-Creator aligns to serve the unfolding potential, an essential characteristic of an Ambassador.

It is the time of year when the sunflowers are in bloom. Powdery pollen sticks to the thick nectar; it's the mother lode for a busy bee colony! The big yellow-petaled heads of the sunflower keep their face to the sun as it moves across the sky. With thousands of bees, pounds of pollen, gallons of nectar, and hundreds of moving targets, it takes a well-coordinated effort for us to turn it all into bee's gold—honey!

I see the school bus stop; Girl hops out of the bus, her overstuffed backpack bounces on her back as she jogs down the long driveway and into the house. Taking a break from administrating the bee crowd, I buzz over to a hibiscus bush near the kitchen window. Girl and Mother are sitting at the table.

"Mom, there is going to be a contest this month to write a children's book. The best story wins a new set of water skis and a pull rope. That'll be amazing this summer!"

"Wow, great, dear! What are you thinking? Do you have any ideas for a storyline?"

"I don't know yet; I'll have to spend some time in my old Pondering Chair and see what I come up with." Girl got up, grabbed a cookie and a carrot, headed out the door to do chores and ponder with Pony. I flew ahead to my honey jar to wait.

After finishing up the chores, she made her way to Pony's stall and took a seat in her chair. She glanced up at a shelf where she kept her Merkabah World keepsakes and stood back up. She put the seashell in her shirt pocket, wrapped the snake bracelet around her arm and held the scroll in her hand, then sat back down.

"Wow, if these walls could talk, now that would be a story!" said Girl. Then to Pony, "I am looking for a creative idea for a children's book; there is a contest at school, the prize is a new set of water skis!"

"What are water skis, Girl?" asked Pony.

Since they had returned from their last adventure, she could "hear" him by changing the way she listened. Focusing on her heart and what it sensed, she could get a feeling and see an image, then her brain would transform the impression into words. She was starting to listen to people with her heart too. Sometimes, what people say and what she sensed did not match up—they did not speak their truth. The heart knows the whole truth. She was remembering how to align her heart and her head.

The best way to explain waterskiing to Pony was to imagine herself doing it; he could "see" the picture in her brain. When she did this, she also talked because that is what humans do, which helped Pony expand his vocabulary. Pony felt excitement attached to the image of Girl and the water skis.

"Oh, I understand now, it looks like you are having fun, but it's not for horses!"

Girl noticed she was thinking so hard; she was holding her breath. She exhaled, took another deep breath, closed her eyes, and began to meditate, opening the portal to the In-Between and the passageway to the Merkabah World. A yellow swirl appeared in the middle of the stall, and little by little—breath by breath—the passage opened. I took my place on Pony's forelock; he glanced back at his tail, Girl grabbed it, and he jumped into the portal headfirst with Girl flying behind; she was getting the hang of this!

$$\triangle \nabla \triangle \nabla \triangle \nabla \triangle \nabla$$

The In-Between was a beckoning yellow carpet of light gliding on top of twisting green, pink, and blue ropes. We rode the waves through; Girl was hooting and hollering like she was riding in a rodeo. Eventually, the passageway brought us to a group campsite overlooking a valley surrounded by tall snow-covered mountains. Seven tents circled a fire pit; a big, black iron stew pot hung empty from a tripod over unlit logs—

clusters of trees with mushroom-shaped canopies scattered sporadically across the valley's tall, golden grass carpet. My bee sense got a whiff of flowering teak trees, nectar I've not tasted for quite some time. A pair of lakes, separated by a strip of land, shimmered in the center of the valley.

"The place looks empty." Girl noted, wandering around the circle of tents looking for some sign of life when the ground started to vibrate. "Look, zebras!" Girl said, pointing down toward the valley.

Headed for the lakes, a hundred or more zebras parted the golden sea of grass. The herd gradually came to a stop along the shores of each lake. More animals began to appear and gather around the lakes. Lions lounged and licked their cubs, a plentitude of pink flamingos perched on one leg in the shallows, rhinoceros wallowed in the cool mud. Wildebeests wandered in; hiding hippopotamuses popped their heads up out of the water, hyenas eyed the gathering from afar, and to complete the party, a pair of cheetahs stretched out in the shade under a flowering teak tree.

It was a wildly wonderful gathering of creatures that hunt, creatures that munch, and creatures that eat others for lunch, all peacefully assembled at the Twin Lakes.

A big *ZIPPING* noise from behind us turned our attention to one of the tents. The door was open. A luminous presence floated out, followed by a woman with skin as dark as the moonless night sky. She was cloaked in a long, yellow, ornately-embroidered kaftan. A yellow feather clung to her blizzard of snow-white hair.

"Mind what happens," she whispered.

The iridescent cloud began to vibrate and glow bright yellow; she closed her blue eyes and took a blind step into the light-filled cloud. The light became her, and she became the light. She opened her eyes; they were now violet, "Welcome, we are Mawu."

I flew up and landed on the yellow feather in her hair.

Girl's blue eyes were wide, Pony's were wider, they stood there as still as statues. They were remembering the same thing: *the power of two becoming one.*

"We welcome you to this land. I am Mawu." She nodded at Pony and Girl; her elegant hand opened, as she pointed toward the mountains on the horizon and turned in a slow circle, tracing the 360° view of the valley below us with her finger. "We are the leader of this land. We are the teacher of this land. We are the student of this land. We are one with this land. We create with this land."

"Pleased to meet you, Mawu," Girl finally spoke, blinking her eyes in wonder. "What was that light?"

"It is my sacred twin, my Soul." She raised both arms now and moved them through the air in a sideways figure eight.

"I am directionless bones, muscles, organs, and skin without the light of my twin. Without this body my twin has no arms or legs to fulfill its purpose. United, body and Soul, we are more than the sum."

"How do I connect to my light, my Soul?" Girl wondered.

"You already are, dear. Do you remember how you got here?"

"By pondering—that's what I call meditating, I've done it since I was a small child. When I have a question about something, I sit in my Pondering Chair, close my eyes, relax my body into quietness and breathe. I breathe 'out' with the question and 'in' with the answer. I feel a tingling sensation in my body when I hear the answer. Sometimes when I am pondering, an opening appears in Pony's stall, and Pony takes me through it. That's how we got here."

"See, dear, you are connecting to your energetic body— your Soul and welcoming its guidance. Answers that we seek lie within us, just waiting for us to ask. You are one of the wise ones, dear; many humans travel through life searching for an elusive light at the end of the tunnel, but what they must remember is that they are the light." Her violet eyes sparkled.

Mawu started to sing; she began to move her body slowly and rhythmically.

"The twins of Body and Soul

Spirit on a mission remains one part of the whole

Embodied in a perfect partner, together, they can do what is asked to be done

These twins aligned as one, are more than the sum."

The enchanting tune hung in the air; she began down the path that led to the lakes.

"In nature, there are many twins. Let's explore."

The path turned back and forth, in and out of trees. A gentle wind wove through the branches; it whispered her name, "Mawu."

The path ended under an enormous tree anchored on the narrow strip of land between the lakes. Knobby roots reached out from the wide trunk to the water's edge of both lakes. Vines with yellow flowers spiraled down from its branches, touching the surface of the lakes. The congregation of animals around the Twin Lakes watched us with curiosity.

"How can so many animals, predators, and prey, be here together in peace?" Girl asked.

"This is not the time to eat; it is the time to connect, to remember they are one, one part of the whole," she explained.

The animals started to shift; something was happening. Attention turned to the zebras. A zebra mare stepped to the side of the larger herd and laid down on the ground.

"The zebra is about to give birth; mind what happens," whispered Mawu.

After a few minutes, a zebra foal was born in the golden grass. The lions instinctually looked that way but did not move. The mother zebra stood up; the foal could not. The foal tried to stand on his legs, moving awkwardly, practicing, building strength.

A female lion yawned, stretched her front legs, paws to claws. The two cubs at her side, like their mother, yawned and stretched from paws to claws. The lioness started to make her way toward the foal, then she sat back on her haunches, licked her nose with her pink tongue, the cubs did the same. All eyes were on the foal. Moments seemed like hours as the newborn foal tried over and over to stand. The mare waited patiently, faithfully. The lioness watched the zebra foal with one eye and her cubs with the other; she was also waiting patiently, faithfully.

Then, the foal's effort coordinated, and he came up off the ground on weak, unsteady legs. He wobbled his way to his mother and found her milk. The mare glanced back at the lioness and snorted at her. The lioness and her cubs returned to her pride.

"Tell me what you saw, Girl."

"I saw a baby zebra almost become the victim of a lion. He was lucky to survive, Mawu!"

Pony glanced wisely at Mawu and said, "I saw a foal connect to his spirit, remember who he was, stand up using his own power, not power borrowed from another. I saw a mare teach her foal that he was not born a victim."

Girl nodded at Pony; a new knowing was forming inside of her.

Mawu added, "I saw a lioness teach her cubs what it means to be a fair predator, that it was not time to hunt, but to empower another. *Powering with* creates life, *powering over* ends life."

She began to sing again; her voice carried across the lakes, all eyes were on the great teacher.

"The Twins of Predator and Prey

With the power of faith and connection, the brave will stay

The intent to slay is to balance; it is not to hunt for fun

These twins aligned as one are more than the sum."

Mawu's voice remained lyrical, her arms reached the sky, "The sun and the moon are twins," she began to sing again.

"The Twins of Day and Night

Co-creating a constant cycle of darkness and light

Life forms of the moon are in harmony with life forms of the sun

These twins aligned as one are more than the sum."

As the lyric faded onto a passing breeze, Mawu placed her hands on her head, on her heart, then on her throat.

"Courageous leaders, my dear, are fully aligned with their twin." Mawu began to sing again. "Mind these words, dear."

"The Twins of Being and Becoming

Uncovering why you are here will be what keeps you running

Live fully in every moment; your heart keeps the cadence like a drum

These twins aligned as one are more than the sum."

The notes danced on the leaves sparking memories. Girl leaned against Pony and wondered what was to come. She could feel the power within the oneness of her twin.

Mawu continued humming the tune, pulled the yellow feather, with me still on it, from her drift of white hair, drew a circle in the air, opening the yellow portal to the In-Between. I buzzed around the swirling opening. Girl quietly slid onto Pony's back, wrapped her arms around his neck. Mawu placed the feather in her left hand.

"Mind these words, twins aligned are more than the sum, dear."

Girl nodded. "Thank you, Mawu."

Pony jumped through into the beckoning yellow passageway—the space filled with yellow blazing ropelike lights of potential.

$$\Delta \nabla \Delta \nabla \Delta \nabla$$

The following day, the sun was shining through the old honey jar. Pony and I were waiting; we knew. Girl came into the barn early. She had a pad of paper, a pen, and a big idea.

"Pony, I had a dream about the Twin Lakes last night; I know what to write for the book writing contest."

She moved a bale of hay in front of her Pondering Chair to use as a table, opened her notebook, and was ready to write.

But, nothing came, all of her ideas had vanished, her brow wrinkled, she gave Pony a worried look.

"What if they don't like the story, what if people think it's a crazy idea, now I don't know where or how to start."

Pony picked up the yellow feather from the souvenir shelf with his lips and brought it to Girl. When she took the feather from Pony, she noticed it was a feather pen; she wrote "remember." The ink was violet. She smiled and whispered, "Thank you, Mawu."

She started again, first closing her eyes and breathing out and in, out and in; the message came to her, and she knew what to write. Pony stood behind her, softly breathing on her neck as she wrote.

Chapter 6

The Processor – Emotional Resilience

Processing life's experiences into wisdom creates an evolved Ambassador.

I t was a glowing day, not too hot and not too cool, the perfect time of year. Bees love days like this; an empty blue sky holds limitless possibilities for what wants to happen. With the day's pollen contribution coming from sunflowers, lilacs, apple blossoms, and clover, anything was possible! This potpourri of pollen will make exceptionally delicious honey. I had just taken a new bee body; I felt strong and had the urge to get busy!

After making a large pollen drop, I flew to my observation spot just outside the kitchen window. Girl finished breakfast and was ready to head off to school.

"Bye, Mom and Dad, I'm going to walk to school today. It's early; I have time to stop at the park," Girl said, as she walked out of the house and headed down the driveway. I buzzed along behind her.

Even though she was getting older, she still loved to swing with her head leaned back, joining to the rhythm of everything around her. Today, with each pump of her knees, she admired her newly modified bell-bottom jeans. She liked the retro look of things; the 60s especially. Yesterday, she cut a slit up to the knee on the outside of the jeans and sewed in a large triangular piece of flowered material to make wide bell-bottoms. They looked so cool! Topping off the look was a peace sign necklace she found at a garage sale.

Right on time, the bell rang as she took her seat. Home economics, English, and science passed by quickly, and then it was time for lunch. While waiting in the line for the day's delicacy of "porchoplets," instant mashed potatoes, and canned peas, *Yummy,* Girl thought, sarcastically; three girls from her class approached her.

"Yeah, Mod Squad—super groovy threads!" teased Tormentor #1—nicknamed Braces.

"Did you get that outfit from your mom's closet? P-U it smells like it! Or is it your style that is so old it smells?!" added Tormentor #2—nicknamed Freckle Face.

These three girls were a mean little clique, the kind that teases anyone they consider different. She tried to ignore them by looking interested in the dessert options.

"Hippies are out, you know, Mod Squad, they used to be cool, but now they are just cold and dead!" Tormentor #3—

nicknamed Red Pig Tail—said too loudly, students waiting in line started to laugh.

Girl took her tray over to a corner table and ate lunch alone, pretending to read a book. She used her hand to cover her brow, so they would not see her angry tears. That anger formed a big grudge in her heart, not leaving room for much else, including dessert.

After school, she headed directly for the barn; she needed some Pony time.

"Pony, I have a question." She sat down in her Pondering Chair; Pony stopped munching on hay.

"Girl, you humans are a curious species. What is the question?" asked Pony.

"Those mean girls at school were at it again, I feel so angry, and it is getting harder to let it go. My mom says, 'Dear, don't go down to their level.' Why do we hold grudges anyway?"

"It is in the way you hold on to old emotion," Pony explained to his student. "Animals use emotion for information to survive. We feel the emotion for what it is, like any other body message. We get the message behind the emotion, act in response to the emotion, and let it go, so we are ready for the next moment. If we are hungry, we eat—thirsty, drink—angry, set a boundary—sad, cry—scared, we run. If we held on to these emotions, we would be so preoccupied trying to keep these unresolved emotions contained—*that turn to grudges, by the way!*—we would not notice a predator sneaking up on us." Pony finished his speech and grabbed a bite.

"Oh, one more thing," Pony kept right on munching while he communicated his thoughts, "remember we have 60 million years of practice, and you humans only have 6 million. You're learning, caterpillar!"

"That makes sense." Girl sat up in the chair like a good student. "Tell me about letting go; that is the hard part for me."

"Well, think of it like eating hay. We eat it, digest it, and then we go poop." Girl laughed; Pony was funny sometimes! "As a horse, I sense emotions in beings all around me; I have to; my life depends on it. If you are scared, that means I should be scared; we need to look for safety. If you are sad, that is information for me to comfort you. Emotions are nature's common language; they are how we create connection. Disconnection creates division; division creates opportunities for predators to attack."

I could sense Girl putting the pieces together from my resting spot on top of the old honey jar. There was silence for a few minutes. The sun was shining in through the window, a beam of light passed through the empty honey jar, the remains of the honey gave the light an orange glow.

"Let's take a trip. Emotions. That is the topic." Girl closed her eyes, started to breathe deeply, out and in, out and in— her breath connecting to the sky, the earth, to all that was around her.

The sunlight expanded into an orange spiraling passageway. I flew over to Pony's forelock. Girl opened her eyes, winked at Pony, hopped on his back, and we jumped into the portal.

$$\triangle \triangledown \triangle \triangledown \triangle \triangledown$$

The In-Between world felt soft, cushioned; it was pulsating, lub-dub, lub-dub. We seemed to be underwater as if we were inside a womb. Pony's legs moved in slow motion; Girl's hair was floating in the watery environment. Human babies of all colors were swimming with us. Some of the babies were crying; some were laughing, some looked hungry, some were grinning. Girl reached out to the emotional parade of babies as they passed by. After nine minutes of floating, the time was right, and we were pushed out of the In-Between onto a green field frosted by orange flowers.

"It smells wonderful here!" Girl turned in a circle with her arms stretched wide; face turned up to the blue sky. "I wonder what will happen here! What will we learn here! Pony, remember our first adventure? We didn't know what to expect, and it seemed scary, now *not knowing* what to expect is exciting!"

Pony sampled the grass and flowers; he looked up at Girl; his muzzle was covered with orange pollen. Suddenly, he stopped chewing; a long blade of grass hung from his mouth like a green straw. His ears perked up.

"Hear that, Girl? Take a look, see what you can see." Girl hopped up on his back; she pointed towards the sound.

"It's music, coming from over there. Let's head that way, Pony."

We waded through the sea of grass. The field started to roll up a hill, and from the top of the hill, we could see where a forest met the orange-topped green field, and off we went into the trees.

Inside the forest, the air became still but not quiet. The graceful musical melody harmonized with the sounds in the woods. Butterflies and dragonflies flitted about; sunlight highlighted their divinely-created wings. Flying insects are quite a feat of Mother Nature, wouldn't you say? We moved inside the forest, following the music to a meadow. A red caboose sat in the middle of the clearing. Near the caboose, there was a fire pit surrounded by old tree stumps. A big, black metal pot hung from a tripod over the fire. The music was coming from inside of the caboose.

"This is a nice place to camp." Girl peaked into the pot. "It's full of bones, boiling in water. That's odd."

The door to the caboose opened. A lady with tousled gray hair stepped down the grated iron steps; she wore a skirt, layered in patches, like a treasured family quilt. Her white linen blouse tucked into the skirt; strands of thick string spiraled together cinching a black leather belt around her waist.

"I have a knowing that you are here to learn about emotions." She winked and walked over to Girl. "I think I can help with that! So happy to have you here. Happy—that's an emotion—what do you think of that?"

Girl's eyes were wide. "Happy? I suppose that means everything is just fine, as it should be."

"Yes, happiness is a sense of wellness right now at this moment; it cannot be chased; you'll never catch it," she stated. "Welcome, I am Estella."

"Nice to meet you; thank you for having us; I am happy to be here! I am also curious, why are you boiling a pot of bones, Estella?"

"Pull up a seat around the fire, dear." Estella poked at the fire with a long stick; orange sparks floated up in the air. "I will tell you about the bones—they are the waste product of emotion. Emotions get stuck in our bones if we don't toss them out." Pony yawned and nodded at the girls as they talked about emotions. I got comfortable in his forelock, ready for the story of the bones.

A soft breeze circled the clearing, lifting fallen leaves with its invisible fingers. Girl could sense something watching.

Estella waved her hand toward the edge of the forest and said, "Come on, you are welcome to join us!" Rabbits, deer, a grand elk with an owl on his antlers, raccoons, possums, birds, foxes, and a black bear came out of the forest. They created a circle around the caboose and the pot of boiling bones.

"What emotion do these forest creatures have? What do you feel surrounding you?" asked Estella.

Girl sensed the gathering of wildlife. She closed her eyes, took a few deep breaths. "I feel curiosity all around me."

"Your curiosity is contagious; you drew them here. All emotions are contagious, contagiously connecting. Emotion is a universal language; it is understood across species. Even when we do have a common spoken language, we communicate much more through emotion." Estella nodded at the diverse gathering.

"If I were to shoot a rifle now, fear would be the contagion that connects, and they would all run." Girl's eyes grew wide at the thought of how quickly something as extraordinary as curiosity could change to fear.

"The information behind an emotion is essential for survival, and emotion is a predictor of the future. Fear = run; if you don't run, you can die. Curiosity = learning something new; adding to the knowledge base of a species." Estella got up and threw another log on the fire to keep the bones boiling. "Processing emotion makes us resilient, dear, as an individual and as a species."

Girl looked at the animal menagerie of Mother Nature's creations that surrounded her, all curiously content and connected. At this moment, that was all that mattered.

"Undigested emotions are like old stew bones sitting in your heart and can sink deep into your very essence. A pot full of yesterday's bones has no room for today's stew." Estella's words hung in the air before dissolving into the steam rising from the boiling bones. "You become what you carry in your heart, dear."

"But it can be so hard to let go of grudges when people are so mean. I take things too personally, I suppose." Girl contemplated the foundation of how a grudge starts.

"Yes, dear, if the emotion is not stuck in you, you can start each day with a clean heart. Let go of the emotions from old stories; if not, you become your stories. When someone makes a terrible mistake, they can live like a mistake or become wiser for it." Estella winked at Pony. "Appreciating the wisdom removes the bone from your heart." The end of a bone popped up out of the boiling water.

A murmur arose from the gathering of animals. Mutterings from each of them blended together creating a collective aha moment, supporting Girl's new knowing. Then there were a few moments of silence, as they watched the flames reaching for the bottom of the pot.

"Let's dump out these old bones and make a new stew!" She grabbed a long sturdy stick. "Everyone, stand back." She placed the stick through the handle to the other side. "Grab the other end of the stick, dear. Let's bury these old bones!"

Estella and Girl lifted the black pot off the fire and dumped it into a hole behind the caboose. They brought the empty pot back and set it on the hook of the iron tripod, and that was that.

"I'll be right back." Estella went into the caboose.

The forest animals started moving around, mingling as humans do after an important meeting. Pony made his way over to them. He has an instinctual capacity to create connection; the more diverse a group is, the better their chance of survival.

Estella came out of the caboose carrying bags overflowing with various vegetables and a big wooden spoon stuck in her belt. "We've had enough talk of bones for today; let's make a vegetarian stew, flavored with a special mixture of spices handed down from my grandmother."

Girl and Estella chopped, diced, and spiced, then sat quietly, waiting for the stew to bubble. I noticed a hint of orange blossom in the spice, an interesting flavor for stew!

After enjoying the stew, Girl and Estella shared a familiar embrace. The forest animals blended back into the forest. It was time to leave the Merkabah World.

"Oh, dear, take this packet of spice, use it in your next pot of stew." Estella handed her an orange cloth bag stuffed full of the family's spice.

Girl thanked Estella, put the precious gift in her zippered pocket, and waved goodbye; Pony swished his tail as we turned to leave. Across the clearing toward the edge of the forest, the swirling orange passageway opened before us, and we walked right in.

In the In-Between, Girl's legs moved in sync with Pony's, moving together back through the watery space without an up or a down or an above or below. We passed over floating bones and ducked under floating bones—we left those old bones behind and came through the other side into Pony's stall feeling fresh and renewed.

△▽△▽△▽

The next day on the way to school, Girl stopped at the swings again; she began to swing high, toes touching the sky. She let herself feel the anger from the day before; she knew what to do to clear the bones of the three tormenters. Remembering Estella's advice, she would process the anger to start the day with an empty heart. She visualized Braces, let herself be open to what wanted to be noticed in the anger. Braces felt ugly; she sensed it now. Anger towards Braces turned to compassion. Freckle Face felt like she did not belong; her skin was not smooth; it was speckled with freckles, her anger turned to acceptance. Back and forth, she swung. She sensed it, felt it easily now; Red Pig Tails felt unloved; anger turned to love. The anger was released; it was not hers, to begin with. She had emptied the bones from her pot. She went into school with an open heart, ready for the day.

She brought her lunch that day; it was leftover stew her mother made. It had a hint of orange in the flavor. *Interesting,* she thought, *the recipe must have been passed down from Estella!* When the three tormentors walked by, she smiled and nodded a greeting to them. They left her alone to eat the stew in her newly-found peace.

76

Chapter 7

The Protector – The Right to Be

Trust the Protector and be brave. Bravery is an essential trait of an Ambassador.

It was graduation day. Girl's family was returning home from the afternoon ceremony. She was still dressed in her graduation cap and gown, holding a bouquet of red roses.

"I'll be in later, Mom; I want to spend some time with Pony." She headed to the barn. I followed and took a spot on the same old honey jar.

"Pony, well, I've done it, graduated, and now what do I do? I've waited a long time for this day, but now that it's here, I am not sure I want to leave for college. I don't want to leave you."

"Dear, I will always be with you and there for you. I always have been, and I always will be. You will always be mine, and you will be fine!" Pony assured her.

She sat down in her chair and began to ponder, revisiting the day in her mind enough to let it go for the moment. She needed some Merkabah World time; maybe there she'd find some clarity. As she relaxed into her breath, she willfully opened a passageway to explore. The portal was red, as red as her roses.

$$\triangle\triangledown\triangle\triangledown\triangle\triangledown\triangle\triangledown$$

The In-Between's twirling red ropes of light guided her past a life to come and a life well-lived. Bell-bottom jeans floated by, swings swinging by themselves, honeybees, horses, zebras, lions, owls, babies, monkeys, an erupting volcano, a unicorn, a giant purple octopus's arms waved them along. More things appeared, Virgin Mary statues, little dogs and big dogs, books with pages turning, old men, old women, gangs of teenagers, a Christmas tree, a sailboat with a lizard, a compass, a river running in circles, an angel with purple wings, it was all as familiar as it was strange.

The In-Between's passageway opened up onto a dirt road. Girl landed alone, without Pony. I was already there, waiting for her.

"Pony, Pony, where are you!" she called out in alarm, wanting to turn back, but the portal was closed.

Just ahead, a long driveway, lined with magnolia trees, beckoned to her. Glossy green leaves of the magnolias cupped, white, complexly-petaled flowers. Pastures rolled their way to meet the forest.

Girl began her way up the road; around the first turn, a horse was waiting for her in the middle of the driveway, a chestnut stallion, it was me. No longer Bee.

"Hello, sir," she greeted me.

"Hello, Dear One," I replied. "Walk with me, and I will walk with you." And we walked side by side along the drive in the shade of the magnolias.

"Do I know you, sir? I feel as though we've met," inquired Girl. My presence as a stallion was bold; in my royal presence, I knew she felt very safe.

"Yes, you know me. You are mine and will always be mine. I take many forms, even as a bee. You can call me Juano or Dorado; you can call me Pony; you can call me Husband, Mother, Father, Grandmother, Aunt, or Uncle, I work through them; I am your Protector," I replied.

Girl nodded but was confused, "Why, why do I need your protection? What makes me so important?"

"Dear, during your lifetime, you will encounter things that may jeopardize your reason for being. I carefully allow what must be allowed so you can remember your wisdom. I protect you so that you can learn to trust, to trust enough to be brave." My ears perked up, sensing something to come. "My dear one, your life has already been written; it is up to you to follow the signs."

Girl was walking with me, but her mind was elsewhere. She sensed what was shifting in the environment around her; it felt like the energy of the In-Between. She remembered the day when Pony saved me from her father. She remembered the first time she visited the Merkabah World, The Valley of Signs and Wonders; the snake bracelet was on her arm, she touched it and remembered the story of Gerardo and the horse.

She'd lived by her noble truths, guided by the wisdom of Satya. Her connection to nature remained as solid as her memory of riding a unicorn in the ocean. Wonderful and often unexpected possibilities showed up when she aligned with her soul. Understanding the vital purpose of emotion, as she learned from Estella, freed her from shame, igniting her intuitive gifts. Now, here in the Merkabah World, she has met her protector. *Why*, she thought, *am I so important to have such a guardian?*

"I still don't get it; what gives me the right to be part of all of this, worthy of you?" she asked.

"My Dear One, everyone has choices, choices to remember who they were born to be, some listen, some do not, some play a part in your remembering, then you let them go. It is all part of a complex *mission;* that is the best word to describe it. Yes, you are my mission!" I whinnied out loud; it sounded like a laugh. Girl laughed too; she sighed and relaxed.

Up ahead, a house came into view. It was an old white farmhouse; a welcoming circular drive spiraled around a small pond. Its edge was blooming with a mass of white, violet, blue, green, yellow, orange, and red flowers. There was a bench next to the pond. We continued to walk side by side toward the pond. Girl sat on the bench, with me, her protector, standing behind her. It was quiet; the pond's surface was still, shimmering in the sunlight. She could see our reflection, a chestnut stallion at her back, she in her graduation robe.

My stallion head was directly above hers, my powerful chest pushing softly against her back, "You've done well, My Dear One. Your journey has brought you to this place in time."

A gust of wind rippled our reflection. "During your pilgrimage, you have learned to be a Seer, a Balancer, a Sensor, a Co-Creator, a Processor, and a Protector." I lovingly rubbed the top of her head with my muzzle. "Now, you remember the Ambassador you are born to be."

△▽△▽△▽△▽

The pond returned to stillness and Girl's reflection reappeared, but she had changed. Looking back at her was a middle-aged lady with wild, white hair and a violet twinkle in her eye. At her back stood a middle-aged man with a mane of graying, chestnut colored hair, and a violet twinkle in his eye.

"Hi, what's for lunch, Magnolia?" I asked.

Afterword

By Dr. Giselle Faubel

The 21st century is calling for new parables to help us understand our new reality. In a world where progress depends on consciousness and responsibility to prevent our demise, we yearn for human connection like never before. Having been hostages to the unknown, the uncertainty, the unpredictability, and the isolation, caused by recent world events, now we are faced with finding a new way of living.

In every era of civilization, historians have accounted for our vulnerabilities and strengths, realizing how we arrived where we are. Today, in a world where technology prevails, we yearn for the sacred; we look to the skies for answers, and we search within for purpose. The story that landed us here is one we cannot change; however, the story of where we end up is for us to write. Hopefully, the lessons we've learned will prevail and prevent us from engaging in mistakes that we can't afford to repeat. In so doing, open us to the opportunity to become wiser and more enlightened.

The COVID-19 pandemic held humanity hostage by a common threat, yet we struggle to come together as a civilization; it seems we have individually fought to validate the fundamental experience of staying alive. We live in a world of polarities, where we have the capacity for cruelty and compassion, and in the end, it depends on our choices and the values we decide to live by.

This book presents a framework that serves as a platform for a global calling to open our hearts, minds, and Souls to make the world a better place. It sounds so simple, an awareness that we can no longer avoid. We must accept the challenge of waking up to a new worldview with new perspectives and higher consciousness.

In *Pony's Girl Parables*, Girl adventures between worlds seeking answers to questions she initially does not understand. Through her travels, we are offered the possibility of finding our answers by examining our own lives and seeking our truth. Girl connected with the collective "knowing" and remembered the purpose of her existence. It is the invitation for us to travel into our knowing and reflect upon our own life experience so we, too, can become enlightened.

We must learn to recognize the leaders who will guide us in action, allow ourselves the courage to ask for help; because only when we acknowledge our vulnerabilities will we be able to connect with our strengths. Sometimes, our supporters are enlightened ones aware of the power of connection and the benefits to the whole; sometimes, they serve the higher good unbeknownst to them. Whatever the case, the result is a progressing sense of awakening that helps us see darkness and light the inevitable transformation's emergence.

$$\triangle\triangledown\triangle\triangledown\triangle\triangledown$$

Dr. Faubel holds a Bachelor of Science degree in Psychology from Boston College, A Master's degree in Counseling and Consulting Psychology from Harvard University, and a Doctorate in Psychology from Miami Institute of Psychology. After teaching at the American University in London, England, for three years, she returned to the USA to open a practice supported by her herd of horses. In addition to her private practice, Dr. Faubel is a consulting psychologist for the Florida court system and pro-vides professional services for various corporations.

∆∇∆∇∆∇∆∇

Appendix

Archetype: Ambassador

Life is not a pilgrimage to become an Ambassador, but rather a pilgrimage of remembering the Ambassador one was born to be.

- An Ambassador's heart is filled with endless love. This love comes from a higher source.
- Ambassadors serve, advocate, negotiate for the greatest good of All.
- Ambassadors are evolved leaders. Becoming an evolved leader is a four stage process*:
  - First, we are followers to observe leadership in action
  - Secondly, we become leaders of ourselves
  - Thirdly, we lead others
  - Fourthly, we become followers again—following what is asking to happen, following our potential
- An Ambassador sees unconditionally, using signs, omens, and intuition to understand better what is asking to unfold.

An Ambassador's lifetime is a pilgrimage of experiences—good and bad. He gains the wisdom to lead.

*From Alan Seale's book *Transformational Presence – How to Make a Difference In a Rapidly Changing World.*

$$\triangle\triangledown\triangle\triangledown\triangle\triangledown$$

Chakra: Crown

- Characteristics of Crown Chakra:
  - Color: Violet or White
  - Location: Top of head
  - Element: Thought
  - Right: To know
  - Core Belief: Awareness
  - Attribute: Self-knowledge
  - Affirmations:
    - Divinity resides within me.
    - I am open to new ideas.
    - Information I need comes to me.
    - The world is my teacher.
    - I am guided by a higher power.
    - I am guided by inner wisdom.

$$\Delta\nabla\Delta\nabla\Delta\nabla\Delta\nabla$$

Meditation Audio: https://eponicity.com/ponys-girl-parables-audio-meditations/

Find a comfortable position in a quiet space where you will not be interrupted; distance yourself at least three feet apart if you are with others.

Close your eyes. Exhale all of the air from your lungs.

Exhale just a bit more, blowing the last bit of air from your lungs like a whale or dolphin exhales when they surface.

Now inhale new air, air vital to your life, to your well-being.

Fill your lungs with this air as full as you can.

Take one more little breath to expand your lungs, even fuller than you think is possible...

Hold for four seconds, then fully exhale again, as before. Engage your belly, your ribcage, diaphragm—use all of your resources to move oxygen through your body. Repeat this breath pattern for a few minutes.

Slowly, let your breath return to a regular pattern for a moment. With your eyes closed, notice the sounds you can hear the farthest away from you, note each one.

Now notice the sounds closer to you; note each one.

Now notice the sounds you can hear closest to you.

Can you hear your heart beating?

The movement of your breath? Take notice of what you hear.

Take a few breaths, transitioning to what you feel.

Notice what you can feel in your environment.

The air against your skin.

The clothes on your skin.

Your connection to the ground.

Your connection to the space around you.

Take note of how your feel connected to this space.

Now take a deep transitioning breath, notice what you can smell.

Take note of the different things you can smell around and near you.

Now imagine your breath moving in and out of the top of your head, creating an opening flow between you and all that is above you—let light enter the breath as it moves in and out of you, continue this breathing for a few minutes.

Notice how air and light move through you.

Notice the characteristics of the light.

Now let the light fill your whole body.

Let it move inside of you.

Filling every space, every corner of you, through your core, out through your arms, hands, fingers.

It moves down your spine, your legs, feet, toes.

It flows into your blood and then through your bones, rising up through your skin...

Surrounding you like a capsule of light.

Ask the light to show you what it wants you to know—listen unconditionally, with an open heart.

What comes to you may not make sense; there is no need to do anything, only be receptive.

When you feel it's time, pull the energy inward, into your skin, muscles, blood vessels, organs, and bones. Let it flow, fill you, and flow through your legs and direct it downward, connecting you to the ground, to the earth.

Then let it rise up, creating a vertical column of light connecting you to the universe, to things seen and unseen.

Your body is the conduit for the flowing movement of energy and light as you breathe in and out with the flow.

When you feel ready, open your eyes, and anchor the experience by creating a drawing or journal entry.

△▽△▽△▽△▽

Points to Ponder

1. Do you believe you were born for a reason?
2. Do you sense that you have unseen guides or protection?
3. Can you remember a time when you just knew something was the right decision without having to analyze the pros and cons?
4. Who supports your hopes and dreams?
5. What role does nature play in your life?

△▽△▽△▽△▽

Back Story

The day I knew there was more to the world than meets the eye.

On this day, sometime in 2012, I was working with a family in a small clearing at our (former) retreat center in Costa Rica; Dorado was my equine co-facilitator. It was our third day together, exploring the way family dynamics naturally correlate to herd dynamics. On the previous days, a giant bee was bugging us. It was a tropical species that lives in small colonies consisting of about ten members. They are huge, the size of a ping-pong ball; their ambling flight is clumsy and appears directionless. By this, the third day, the bee was buzzing around us again; I shooed it away, but it just came back. I decided I was going to have to kill it. Although they are not aggressive when they sting, it is excruciating; I didn't want anyone to get stung.

The five of us were standing in a circle, me, the family of three, and Dorado, who was at liberty (not tied up) in the small open arena. I aimed to swat the bee down to the ground and step on it, but just as I raised my hand, Dorado stepped in between me and the bee and "grabbed" the bee with his forehead. He proceeded to bounce the bee on his forehead while he trotted to the edge of the clearing. With a toss of his head, he slung the bee into the rainforest, then trotted back to our circle. We all looked at each other, wide-eyed, and wondered if we really saw what we just saw.

Dorado was standing directly in front of me, staring at me. I thanked him for saving us from the bee, but he didn't budge; his steady gaze pierced right through me. Then I realized he had not saved us from the bee; he saved the bee from me. Upon this realization, Dorado relaxed and started eating grass...message received.

$$\triangle\triangledown\triangle\triangledown\triangle\triangledown\triangle\triangledown$$

Chapter 2 - Expanded

Archetype: Seer

Seeing everything unconditionally is essential for an Ambassador.

- The Seer gathers information unconditionally.
- The Seer uses intuition to understand how things fit together.
- The Seer perceives beyond the physical form, curious to discover other meanings.
- The Seer uses all senses to understand from many perspectives.
- The Seer listens for what wants to come through without judgment or conditions.
- The Seer relays unbiased information to best serve what is unfolding.
- The Seer realizes signs, omens, and synchronicities are the universe's means of communication.

$$\triangle\triangledown\triangle\triangledown\triangle\triangledown$$

The Merkabah

The Merkabah is a sacred shape consisting of two intersecting pyramids. In Hasidic Judaism, its meaning is a multilayered concept that offers us insight into the nature of humanity, the ecosystems of Earth, and the universe. The word "merkabah" in Hebrew means chariot. The Merkabah reminds us of our own potential when we unite our body and Soul.

$$\triangle\triangledown\triangle\triangledown\triangle\triangledown\triangle\triangledown$$

Chakra: Third Eye

- Characteristics of Third Eye Chakra:
  o Color: Indigo
  o Location: Center brow area
  o Element: Light
  o Right: To see
  o Core Belief: Intuition, imagination
  o Attribute: Self-reflection
  o Affirmations:
    ▪ I see all things in clarity.
    ▪ I am open to the wisdom within.
    ▪ I can manifest my vision.
    ▪ I notice signs and wonders.

$$\triangle\triangledown\triangle\triangledown\triangle\triangledown\triangle\triangledown$$

Meditation Audio: https://eponicity.com/ponys-girl-parables-audio-meditations/

Find a comfortable position in a quiet space where you will not be interrupted; distance yourself at least three feet apart if you are with others.

Close your eyes. Exhale all of the air from your lungs.

Exhale just a bit more, blowing the last bit of air from your lungs like a whale or dolphin exhales when they surface.

96

Now inhale new air, air vital to your life, to your well-being.

Fill your lungs with this air as full as you can.

Take one more little breath to expand your lungs, even fuller than you think is possible.

Hold for four seconds, then fully exhale again, as before. Engage your belly, your ribcage, diaphragm—use all of your resources to move oxygen through your body. Repeat this breath pattern for a few minutes.

Now slowly, let your breath return to a regular pattern for a moment.

Open your eyes, look around you, notice your environment as if for the first time.

Notice patterns and shapes.

Notice textures by seeing and touching.

Notice the space between the objects.

What forms does the space in between create?

Notice lines that create the shapes, lines that curve, lines that are straight.

See everything without judging as good or bad, ugly or beautiful; only see the space for what it is.

How does this space support you here and now?

Now see the space for the properties you can feel—how does this place feel—what do you sense?

What do your other senses tell you about this space? What can you smell? What do you feel against your skin?

Close your eyes just a bit, letting in only about 30% of light, what wants to be noticed now?

What has changed in your perception of the environment?

Now start to turn your vision inward; imagine looking at a point at the tip of your nose; as you visualize it, begin to close your eyes, drawing the point up and into the space in the center of your brow, to the space between your eyes.

This is your 3rd eye space. Imagine your breath coming in and out of this space, send it oxygen, be open to the awareness it holds.

What do you notice here?

What can you see here?

Keep your head straight and steady, focused on the 3rd eye space.

Notice what your 3rd eye sees behind you?

Do you see an image, a word, a color? No need to do anything, only notice what is asking to be seen.

Now using your 3rd eye, look to your left—keeping your head straight ahead—breath into the space to your left—take note of what wants to be seen.

Do you see an image, a word, a color? No need to do anything, only notice what is asking to be seen.

Now breathe into the space to your right—what information can be gathered from the space to your right using only your intuition?

Do you see an image, a word, a color? No need to do anything, only notice what is asking to be seen.

Move your attention to the space directly in front of you; eyes remain closed; what information lies there, asking to be noticed?

Do you see an image, a word, a color? No need to do anything, only notice what is asking to be seen.

Take your time—seeing and sensing into the space of the Seer

As a Seer all is seen and sensed unconditionally, everything is information.

When you are ready, anchor the experience by drawing or journaling.

$$\triangle\nabla\triangle\nabla\triangle\nabla$$

Points to Ponder

1. How would your life be different if you saw everything and everyone without condition or judgment?
2. How do you use your imagination in your day-to-day life?
3. Where do you feel intuition in your body?
4. Have you ever overridden your intuition? What happened?
5. How do you know when you are aligned with your intuition?

$$\triangle\nabla\triangle\nabla\triangle\nabla$$

Back Story

In Costa Rica, there is a town located in a pass between the Pacific slope and the Atlantic slope, on the continental divide. We were looking for some land in that area and found a unique valley called Espíritu Santo. This is the Valley of Signs and Wonders in Chapter 2. We did not buy it; however, it is now part of the national park system.

Here is the true story of Gerardo.

A few years ago, I took a group of four guests to have an authentic Costa Rica ranch experience at a friend's cattle ranch. The ranch bordered Nicaragua, where the terrain is flat, and the pastures are often partly swamps. The rancher, Gerardo, a stout, weathered man just past middle age, greeted us with a smile, but no English! He had on the traditional white canvas rancher hat, a machete in a leather sheath tied around his waist with a rope, and white, rubber, knee-high boots.

The horses were ready for us; he helped us get mounted. I was last. He presented me with a tall, dark bay, rough-looking gelding. His head and nose were markedly scarred; however, his eyes and coat shone in the morning sun, he would do.

"Debbie, you are the first person, the only person who can ride this horse besides me. I protect him from the possibility that my workers are too harsh on him; I know you are kind. Be careful; he is afraid of plastic bags." He explained as he gave me a leg up.

"Thank you, Gerardo. Plastic bags, ok. What is his name? Gracias, Gerardo."

He wrinkled his forehead, perplexed by the question. He confessed that the horse didn't have a name. I found that odd since all of his other horses had names. He said I could name him if I liked. I decided to call him Suerte (Lucky). He was fine with that.

We helped him round up about 30 head of various sizes of easy-going, dehorned Brahman cattle. Cowboys for a day, we herded them down a muddy road to the lunch stop. At the stop, 20 more Brahmans were trimming the tops off tall, marshy grass in an ominous-looking swamp. They needed to join our herd. He asked if any of us wanted to go in and get them, nope—a swamp in Central America—above our pay grade!

Gerardo laughed. He'd do it. The mare he was riding was too short for the deep, swamp water, and he asked if we could switch horses. I nodded; of course, he could. He hopped off his beloved, Geraldine, and up on The Horse With No Name—Lucky. From under the shade of some coconut palms, we witnessed them work together.

What, by appearance, was a man and a horse, was not. There was no separation of species; they moved together like one organism. I realized it never occurred to him to name the horse because it would have been like naming his arm or leg. The horse was an extension of him; they were one heart.

While watching the show, we enjoyed a traditional ranch hand lunch: rice, beans, and a hard-boiled egg wrapped together in a banana leaf, tied with a string like a present. They finished in about 15 minutes. It would have taken the gringo—wannabe cowboys—an hour, that is, if we survived being attacked by jungle swamp creatures. Still mounted, he pulled his machete out of its sheath, wacked down a green coconut for each of us, chopped off the top. Inside a refreshing liquid, agua de pipa was just what we needed to sip on while we listened to the story of The Horse With No Name.

About six months prior, he was at the weekly cattle auction, a sickly-looking horse destined for the meat processing plant caught his eye. He caught the horse's eye as well. The horse's doomed gaze haunted him the rest of the afternoon.

At the end of the auction, Gerardo got in his truck to head home but doubled back. Pulling up next to the cab of the cattle truck, he gave the meat man $200 for the horse. It went against all his logic; what use would this old nag be to him? He tied a rope around the horse's neck, squeezed him through the cargo of wide-eyed Brahmans and less fortunate horses; now it was time to go home.

The gelding was bones and skin; the scars on his head, face, body, and the lumps on his swayed back were living evidence of a difficult life. Through the town grapevine, he discovered that the horse was previously owned by a mean drunk, who used the horse to sneak into farms at night and steal cattle.

He nursed the horse back to health; once recovered, he began to work with him on the ranch. I thought to myself, *Who is the lucky one?*

One day at a community event, Gerardo told me that Lucky had died.

He told me what had happened. A few months after the day on the ranch, Gerardo and The Horse With No Name were working with a herd of mature, 2000-pound bulls. They maneuvered the bulls into a small corral used to funnel livestock onto a truck for transport. Without warning, an angry bull charged Gerardo; his chest was the target of the bull's meter-long horn.

Gerardo's agile, quick-witted partner deliberately reared up to block the attack. The horn missed its mark, instead piercing the horse's soft belly. The fatally wounded horse looked back at his Soul mate. Again, at death's door, they were eye to eye. But, this time, Gerardo saw not death but gratitude. As he fell, the horse carefully positioned his body to shield Gerardo from the bulls, leaving just enough room for him to roll under the fence to safety, valiantly saving his savior.

With the same puzzled look he had when he told me that he had not named the horse, he asked me, "Debbie, you know how horses think; why, why did that critter sacrifice himself for me?"

"Gerardo, because you saved him first." He sighed, looked past me, his brow line smoothed, as if seeing something for the first time, then his forlorn heart partnered with his tears of belief; horses are sentient beings.

I facilitated a group of participants on an equine retreat about six months later and planned a farm experience as part of their program. As typical in any small community, everyone knows everything that is going on. I got a call; it was Gerardo. He told me he could arrange a cultural experience at his other farm for my group. We could do some ranch-type work, but not with cattle, with horses. He had heard that in this group, there happened to be two equine vets.

We had a fun ride over to his farm, enjoyed surreal views of the volcano, at times racing each other over rolling, green hills, some still graced with patches of rainforest. The subject horses were in the lower pasture; we herded them into a small holding area. The 10 skin and bone horses, including two mares with nursing foals, were covered with ticks and had split overgrown hooves. They were not long from communing with St. Francis of Assisi. Embarrassed in front of my clients, I wanted an explanation. I approached Gerardo and asked him why they were in such poor condition.

He gave me a big shiny, heartfelt smile, "Because I saved them yesterday, I bought them off the meat truck."

△▽△▽△▽△▽

Chapter 3 - Expanded

Archetype: Balancer

The Balancer removes what is no longer serving the whole to make room for what wants to happen next, an essential attribute of an Ambassador.

- The Balancer makes decisions that maintain or restore equilibrium.
- The Balancer's responsibility comes in two scenarios:
    - A current imbalance is asking to return to a state of equilibrium.
    - Something new wants to happen, and as a result, there will be a temporary imbalance; equilibrium is regained in a new state of being.
- The Balancer uses wisdom gained from the past to make current choices.
- The Balancer evaluates without judgment.

$$\triangle\triangledown\triangle\triangledown\triangle\triangledown$$

Guide Satya: The word satya is the Sanskrit word for truth.

$$\triangle\triangledown\triangle\triangledown\triangle\triangledown$$

Chakra: Throat

- Characteristics of Throat Chakra:
    - Color: Blue
    - Location: Throat
    - Element: Sound
    - Right: To speak and be heard
    - Core Belief: Communicate truth

- o Attribute: Self-expression
- o Affirmations:
  - I hear and speak my truth.
  - I express myself with clear intent.
  - My voice is necessary.
  - I deserve to be heard.

△▽△▽△▽△▽

Meditation

Audio: https://eponicity.com/ponys-girl-parables-audio-meditations/

Find a comfortable position in a quiet space where you will not be interrupted; distance yourself at least three feet apart if you are with others.

Close your eyes. Exhale all of the air from your lungs.

Exhale just a bit more, blowing the last bit of air from your lungs like a whale or dolphin exhales when they surface.

Now inhale new air, air vital to your life, to your well-being.

Fill your lungs with this air as full as you can.

Take one more little breath to expand your lungs, even fuller than you think is possible…

Hold for four seconds, then fully exhale again, as before. Engage your belly, your ribcage, diaphragm—use all of your resources to move oxygen through your body. Repeat this breath pattern for a few minutes.

Slowly, let your breath return to a regular pattern for a moment.

Gently place your hands at your throat, begin to hum the sounds of the alphabet, slowly breathing and moving from letter to letter.

Aaaaaa....baaaa....caaaaa.....daaaa.....eeeee.....faaaa.....

When you get to the letter M, move your hands to your ears, cover your ears while you continue humming the letters.

maaa....naaa....paaa...and so on.

When you finish, breathe normally—put your hands over your heart—relax in this space, still with your eyes closed, for a minute.

Imagine your noble truth appearing in front of you—what is it?

Do you notice an image?

Words?

A sensation?

What do you realize?

Look deeper into your truths, look, listen, go underneath what you are perceiving, what truths lie deep in your being?

What insights to your truths are revealing themselves?

To anchor the experience, journal or draw any insights that may have been realized.

$$\triangle\nabla\triangle\nabla\triangle\nabla\triangle\nabla$$

Points to Ponder

1. How do you make decisions between right and wrong?

2. Where did you learn the difference between right and wrong?
3. What do you do when you have made a mistake or caused another being to suffer?
4. What does "Truth is Balance ~ Balance is Truth" mean to you?
5. What do you need to let go of to be free?

△▽△▽△▽△▽

Back Story

Many experiences intertwine into the content of this chapter. As it was written, section by section, memories came through and were woven into the story. Stella was one of my dearly beloved mares during our time in Costa Rica. She died in a tragic accident, precipitating an unexpected shift in a cultural truth.

Costa Rica has a historically connected culture to the horse; however, they are often seen as a tool for work and status. I had been in Costa Rica for about nine years; I had dedicated, hardworking horsemen caring for the horses and expert guides who kept guests safe on riding excursions. They seemed willing to embrace my philosophy of equine and human collaboration, but I honestly sensed they were kindly placating me; I was just the Crazy Horse Gringa. I organized staff equine facilitated learning workshops to experience a bidirectional relationship with horses for themselves; these experiences started moving things in the right direction. Witnessing the transformation in my equine coaching clients during their time with the horses added weight to the shift.

Stella was the first foal born at our facility. She was a kind, loving horse, and a valued member of our herd. One day she had an accident; she caught her head in a gate and broke a vertebra at the base of her skull. I was not in Costa Rica when it happened. The staff rallied around her and provided around-the-clock care for her for three days in hopes they could save her life, but sadly she had to be euthanized. When I got home, the shroud of grief remained. I organized a debriefing for the staff that included the veterinarian we had at the time. During the debriefing, the vet kept referring to Stella as "the mare" this and "the mare" that—over and over again. I could sense the tension in the room as he rambled on about "the mare" and the efforts to save her life. Suddenly, one of the horsemen stood up, burst into tears, and shouted at him, "She was not just a mare, she was Stella. Stop calling her a MARE! She was loved; she was a part of us."

This tragedy shifted their perceptions. Horses had become sentient in the eyes of these Latino horsemen. Their love for Stella was powerful enough to reshape a culture.

Δ∇Δ∇Δ∇Δ∇

Chapter 4 - Expanded

Archetype: Sensor

- The Sensor appreciates Earth as one whole, living organism, an essential quality for an Ambassador.
- The Sensor observes and senses the environment. In that field of information lies the whole truth.
- The Sensor provides a sense of well-being by constantly monitoring the environment.
- The Sensor collects data from the physical and energetic planes.
- The Sensor perceives and receives information from individuals, groups, societies, and globally.
- The Sensor scans the environment, watching so the community can securely interact, eat, sleep, and do their jobs.
- The Sensor alerts others to move to a place of safety when the need arises.
- The Sensor fosters trust in others.

$$\Delta\nabla\Delta\nabla\Delta\nabla\Delta\nabla$$

Chakra: Heart

- Characteristics of Heart Chakra:
  - Color: Green (high heart color is pink)
  - Location: Heart
  - Element: Air
  - Right: To love and be loved
  - Core Belief: Live connected
  - Attribute: Self-acceptance
  - Affirmations:

- I am worthy of love.
- I love myself and others.
- There is an infinite supply of love.
- I live in balance with others.

$$\Delta \nabla \Delta \nabla \Delta \nabla \Delta \nabla$$

Meditation

Audio: https://eponicity.com/ponys-girl-parables-audio-meditations/

Find a comfortable position in a quiet space where you will not be interrupted; distance yourself at least three feet apart if you are with others.

Close your eyes. Exhale all of the air from your lungs.

Exhale just a bit more, blowing the last bit of air from your lungs like a whale or dolphin exhales when they surface.

Now inhale new air, air vital to your life, to your well-being.

Fill your lungs with this air as full as you can.

Take one more little breath to expand your lungs, even fuller than you think is possible...

Hold for four seconds, then fully exhale again, as before. Engage your belly, your ribcage, diaphragm—use all of your resources to move oxygen through your body. Repeat this breath pattern for a few minutes.

Slowly, let your breath return to a regular pattern for a moment.

Now place your feet flat on the ground.

Feel your feet in contact with the ground.

Connect with the ground through your feet.

Shift your breath, imagine it flowing down your legs and out through your feet, breathe as if your breath is moving in and out through your feet.

Imagine your breath connecting to the Earth.

With each breath, your connection to Earth begins to move up and through you with each breath—exhale to the Earth, inhale from the Earth—Earth becomes your lungs.

Imagine roots of the earth growing into you with each breath.

You are anchored, supported, and nourished by these roots.

These roots connect you to all life on the planet.

Now, while securely held by the roots of Earth, allow your awareness to flow through you, through your body, your core, your neck, and head all the way up reaching to the sky.

Breathe in and out—out and in—as if you are breathing through the top of your head.

The clouds, the sky comes into you, fills you with light.

Now let the breath from the sky meet the breath from the Earth—your breath connects the sky and the Earth—the Earth and the sky.

Rising and falling, rising and falling.

Now move your breath, your light, outward, away from your core—in and out—in and out—your skin becomes part of your breath.

Creating a sphere around you.

Imagine filling the sphere with green light.

What qualities does the light have?

A rhythm, a pulse?

Now expand the sphere to encompass the whole space where you are.

Now expand the sphere to encompass the area 100 feet out from you—while you remain in the center of the sphere—in the beat of your breath.

Now expand your light even further—expand your sphere into your community.

Expand it to your country—send this loving, connecting energy to all of your countrymen.

Now expand your sphere to encompass Earth—an Earth wrapped in this love and light to all of humanity.

Now imagine your light connected to everything on Earth—humans, plants, animals, the air, the soil...

Breathe into this connectedness for a few minutes.

Now open your eyes, and just for a moment, imagine that nothing is connected.

Everything you see is separate, alone.

How do you feel?

What do you notice?

What do you sense?

Notice these sensations for at least one full minute.

Take a deep connecting breath and go back to the reality that everything is connected, breathe here, anchor yourself here; this is where you belong.

Close your eyes again, slowly start to bring your sphere back to yourself. Ground your breath to the earth below you, to the sky above you. Safe, loved, and secure in this sacred space where you are still, and will always be, connected to everything, as everything is lovingly connected to you.

When you are ready, solidify this experience by journaling or create a drawing of what you experienced.

△▽△▽△▽△▽

Points to Ponder

1. What do you feel connected to?
2. Where are there disconnections in your life, and why?
3. What brings you joy?
4. Describe an ecosystem and how it contributes to the whole?
5. Who do you love unconditionally? Who loves you unconditionally?

△▽△▽△▽△▽

Back Story

My grandmother, Martha, passed away in 2021 at the age of 107. She was determined to ride a camel in Egypt and she did at the age of 84.

The first time I visited Costa Rica was in the early 1990s. I was fascinated by the interconnectedness of the rainforest. Professional, naturalist guides opened a whole new world of wonder for me. I realized either everything is connected or nothing is connected. With that realization, something inside of me started to shift. The world as a whole began to speak to me; I felt part of something grander, connected to and a part of Earth. I was curious to learn more.

Earth's electromagnetic field holds immeasurable amounts of information. Migratory patterns, herd behavior on land, schooling in oceans, and flocking behavior in the air are all examples of the electromagnetic field in nature.

The Global Consciousness Project (GCP) has compelling scientific data proving how globally connected humanity is. The GCP measures changes in the human electromagnetic field during major tragedies. For example, they have noted shifts in the field during the events of 911, the death of Princess Diana, devastating natural disasters, the COVID pandemic, and the insurrection of the US Capital on January 6, 2021.

The heart is the biggest receiver and transmitter of electromagnetic energy. Research done by the HeartMath Institute has determined that the electromagnetic field of the heart is 5,000 times greater than the brain's and that the heart field not only scans for information, but it seeks new information. It is the energetic glue that transcends species.

Δ∇Δ∇Δ∇

Chapter 5 - Expanded

Archetype: Co-Creator

The Co-Creator aligns to serve the unfolding potential, an essential characteristic of an Ambassador.

- The Co-Creator uses skills and abilities to create what is needed to serve.
- The Co-Creator partners with others to expand the potential of what is possible.
- The Co-Creator teaches and leads with wisdom, acknowledging that others have come before and others will follow.
- The Co-Creator's forward momentum is powered by infinite potential.
- The Co-Creator's capacity to get things done is fueled by curiosity and inspiration.
- The Co-Creator powers with others, not over others, raising everyone up in the process.

△▽△▽△▽△▽

Mawu

In African mythology, Mawu and Lisa are the twin creators of Heaven and Earth. Mawu, the female, corresponds to the moon and is associated with night, fertility, motherhood, gentleness, forgiveness, rest, and joy. The male twin, Lisa, corresponds to the sun and is associated with daytime; heat, work, power, war, strength, toughness, and stubbornness. Their combined power is more than the sum of the two.

△▽△▽△▽△▽

Chakra: Solar Plexus

- Characteristics of Solar Plexus Chakra:
  - Color: Yellow
  - Location: Just below the sternum
  - Element: Fire
  - Right: To act
  - Core Belief: Power, will
  - Attribute: Self-definition
  - Affirmations:
    - I honor the power within me.
    - I accomplish tasks easily and effortlessly.
    - The fire within me burns through all blocks and fears.
    - I can do whatever I will to do.

△▽△▽△▽△▽

Meditation

Audio: https://eponicity.com/ponys-girl-parables-audio-meditations/

Find a comfortable position in a quiet space where you will not be interrupted; distance yourself at least three feet apart if you are with others.

Close your eyes. Exhale all of the air from your lungs.

Exhale just a bit more, blowing the last bit of air from your lungs like a whale or dolphin exhales when they surface.

Now inhale new air, air vital to your life, to your well-being.

Fill your lungs with this air as full as you can.

Take one more little breath to expand your lungs, even fuller than you think is possible...

Hold for four seconds, then fully exhale again, as before. Engage your belly, your ribcage, diaphragm—use all of your resources to move oxygen through your body. Repeat this breath pattern for a few minutes.

Slowly, let your breath return to a regular pattern for a moment.

Now breathe into the area just below your breastbone, blow out your belly like a balloon with big breaths, belly—in and out-like a Buddha belly, continue this belly breathing for a minute or so.

During this meditation you will ask your Soul to show itself to you.

Your Soul is always with you, it is your spiritual twin. Are you ready?

Ask your Soul to come out of you and show itself to you.

With your eyes closed, but seeing with your eyes closed, invite Soul to show itself in front of you.

What does Soul look like?

Does it have a color?

A shape?

A character?

A smell?

A texture?

Acknowledge your Soul without judgement, with love and appreciation.

Now ask your Soul if it wants you to know anything—does it have a message for you?

Feel free to ask your Soul a question.

Listen to the answer, without judgement, hear your Soul.

Sense, feel, see all there is to see, to know, be with your Soul.

Now, when you are ready, ask your Soul to go back into your body.

Let Soul flow into you, aligning with your body.

Now, this time invite your Ego to come in front of you.

What does it look like?

What form does it take?

What insights come to light as you see your Ego?

How is your Ego being of service to your Soul?

Now ask your Soul to come out again and be next to your Ego.

What do you notice about their differences?

Their interaction?

What message does Soul have for Ego?

What is Ego's reply?

When you are ready, take Ego back into your body, let it fill all of the spaces in your body.

Then invite Soul back into your body, let it fill every space in your body, uniting with Ego.

Now direct your attention to the wholeness of your physical body; how does it feel when it is fully connected to Soul?

Take your time to embrace this alignment of your body and your Soul.

When you are ready, anchor the insights from this experience by drawing or writing in your journal.

△▽△▽△▽△▽

Points to Ponder

1. Where do you feel your Soul lives inside of you?
2. If you could create a twin, what attributes would your twin have that would enhance your life?
3. What does this statement mean to you? "Two aligned as one are more than the sum."
4. Describe an experience when you "powered with" something and an occasion when you "powered over" something. What was the result?
5. Ask yourself, "What wants to happen?" Then take a moment to notice your environment; what catches your eye, is there information in what you are noticing?

△▽△▽△▽△▽

Back Story

This chapter started with the concept of embracing duality. The Hermetic law of polarity teaches us there is duality every-where: life/death, day/night, war/peace, male/female, predator/prey, Ego/Soul, and so on. We often try to live at either end of the spectrum. By embracing both ends, adding them together, our life becomes fuller. Curiosity and creativity lie between the dualities. It is a place where paradoxes are reconciled.

△▽△▽△▽△▽

Chapter 6 - Expanded

Archetype: Processor

Processing life's experiences into wisdom creates an evolved Ambassador.

- The Processor understands emotions are the universal language.
- The Processor knows resiliency comes from getting the message behind emotion, takes action, and then lets it go.
- The Processor is patient and holds space for others to find their inner wisdom.
- The Processor transforms experiences into wisdom.
- The Processor knows emotion is the bridge between the Ego and Soul.

$$\Delta\nabla\Delta\nabla\Delta\nabla$$

Chakra: Sacral

- Characteristics of Sacral Chakra:
  - Color: Orange
  - Location: Pelvic area
  - Element: Water
  - Right: To feel, to want
  - Core Belief: Emotions, sexuality
  - Attribute: Self-gratification
  - Affirmations:
    - I deserve pleasure in my life.
    - I use emotion as information to live authentically.
    - Movement is easy and effortless.

- Things happen in their own time.

$$\Delta\nabla\Delta\nabla\Delta\nabla\Delta\nabla$$

Meditation

Audio: https://eponicity.com/ponys-girl-parables-audio-meditations/

Find a comfortable position in a quiet space where you will not be interrupted; distance yourself at least three feet apart if you are with others.

Close your eyes. Exhale all of the air from your lungs.

Exhale just a bit more, blowing the last bit of air from your lungs like a whale or dolphin exhales when they surface.

Now inhale new air, air vital to your life, to your well-being.

Fill your lungs with this air as full as you can.

Take one more little breath to expand your lungs, even fuller than you think is possible...

Hold for four seconds, then fully exhale again, as before. Engage your belly, your ribcage, diaphragm—use all of your resources to move oxygen through your body. Repeat this breath pattern for a few minutes.

Slowly, let your breath return to a regular pattern for a moment.

Now turn your focus to your bones.

Your skeleton—the frame that holds you up.

Bones give your body form and support—breathe into your bones—let the breath move through your bones—imagine it moving through the spongey material inside your bones.

Now move deeper into this exploration of your bones.

Your bones carry genetic material passed on to and through you, generation after generation—what can you discover there?

What wants to be felt there?

Now, slowly, move your breath out of your bones and into an awareness of your whole body.

The body holds information for us, it is constantly supporting you, taking in information, and provides a buffer zone for our psyche. We will tap into this information by scanning through the body as if in an MRI machine.

Let's begin a scan. As we move through the body, notice sensations, tightness, temperature, or any other feeling in your body as it speaks to you. Do not try to fix it or change what you feel; just notice.

Starting at the top of your head and begin to slowly scan down.

How does your head feel? Skull, scalp?

Notice your face.

Your mouth.

Ears—don't try to fix or change sensations; only notice.

Your throat and neck.

Move to your shoulders—Is there tension there? Don't try to fix it or change it; just notice.

Scan down your back, what sensations are held in your back?

Let your awareness move to the front of your body.

What do you notice in your heart?

In your belly?

Don't try to change or fix; just notice.

Now scan down your arms, hands, and fingers. Do they feel equal? If not, how do they feel different?

Move your awareness to your pelvis; what do you notice here? Just notice, notice how your body talks to you.

Let the scan move down your legs—your feet—heels and toes.

Do they feel equal?

Are you grounded or do you feel like you're floating?

Now, what was the most prominent feeling?

There may have been several notable sensations, for now, pick the one that is calling to be noticed the most.

Go there, back to the most prominent sensation and breathe into that sensation, sending oxygen and awareness to it.

What is it asking you to notice?

Do you see an image?

A word or color?

You may not notice anything, that is information too.

Now take a deeper look under that insight, what lies beneath it? Explore further and further, look deeply down to your bones, go as far as you feel you need to go to get the full message.

When you are ready, go back to that feeling; has it changed in anyway now that you've received the message?

Was something released, understood, reborn in a new way?

Let your breath move with you into this new lightness of being.

If it feels too hard—it's ok—be kind to yourself and just notice what still feels stuck—validate it; it may need more attention, that's ok.

When you feel ready, open your eyes, and anchor the experience by drawing or journaling.

$$\triangle\triangledown\triangle\triangledown\triangle\triangledown$$

Points to Ponder

1. Which emotion is the hardest for you to release?
2. Which emotion did you learn from your parents, and how do you process it?
3. What makes you happy?
4. Which emotion do you find the most contagious?
5. What makes you feel vulnerable? What makes you afraid?

$$\triangle\triangledown\triangle\triangledown\triangle\triangledown$$

Back Story

Growing up in the Midwest, emotion was not a valued commodity but something to be stuffed down deep. The deeper they were stuffed, the braver I was. That all changed when I started working with horses.

For animals, emotion is information essential for survival. My unprocessed emotion was the barrier keeping me from deepening my relationship with horses and people. Most of the time, when working with horses, their "misbehavior" indicates something wrong in the relationship; this is usually an emotion that needs attention. Horses want us to process emotion so we can be fully present—that translates to safety. If I am stewing about something, my anger distracts me from being in the present moment. I'd be the weak link that would not notice a predator sneaking up on the herd.

In my case, half a century of unprocessed emotions were rearing their ugly heads, demanding to be processed. I am an Eponaquest Equine-Facilitated Instructor. Part of the Eponaquest curriculum is the Emotional Message Chart. It is a list of the most common emotions, the message behind the emotion, the questions to ask yourself, and what happens if you ignore the emotion. For example, here are three of the many emotions from the chart.

Emotion	Message	Questions	Intensification
Fear (external threat)	Intuitive, focused awareness of a threat to your well-being.	What is the threat? What action must I take to move to a position of safety?	Worry, Anxiety, Confusion, Dulling of the senses, Panic, Terror, Dissociation
Vulnerability (internal threat to self-image, beliefs, comfortable habits)	Something significant is about to change or be revealed. There is a threat to your comfort zone.	What belief, behavior or perception is being challenged? How might my life change if I move out of my comfort zone or accept this new insight?	Panic, Rage
Anger (boundary violation)	A physical or emotional boundary has been crossed.	What must be protected? What boundary must be established or restored?	Rage, Fury, Deflected rage, Boredom, Apathy

This chart was my bible for about a year. It was a scientific method for me to problem-solve emotions.

The science of epigenetics tells us that experiences can change our genetics; therefore, processing becomes even more critical to pass on wisdom, not trauma, to our offspring.

Δ∇Δ∇Δ∇Δ∇

Chapter 7 - Expanded

Archetype: Protector

Trust the Protector and be brave. Bravery is an essential trait of an Ambassador.

- The Protector has your back.
- The Proctor is there so you can be brave.
- The Proctor ensures a safe environment.
- The Protector, seen or unseen, is there.
- The Protector is the guard for life's pilgrimage.
- The Protector validates your right to be here in this place at this time.

$$\Delta\nabla\Delta\nabla\Delta\nabla$$

Chakra: Root

- Characteristics of Root Chakra:
  - Color: Red
  - Location: Base of spine
  - Element: Earth
  - Right: To be
  - Core Belief: Survival
  - Attribute: Self-preservation
  - Affirmations:
    - It is safe to be here.
    - The earth supports me and meets my needs.
    - I love my body and trust its wisdom.
    - I am immersed in abundance.
    - I am here, and I am real.

$$\Delta\nabla\Delta\nabla\Delta\nabla$$

Meditation

Audio: https://eponicity.com/ponys-girl-parables-audio-medi-tations/

Find a comfortable position in a quiet space where you will not be interrupted; distance yourself at least three feet apart if you are with others.

Close your eyes. Exhale all of the air from your lungs.

Exhale just a bit more, blowing the last bit of air from your lungs like a whale or dolphin exhales when they surface.

Now inhale new air, air vital to your life, to your well-being.

Fill your lungs with this air as full as you can.

Take one more little breath to expand your lungs, even fuller than you think is possible...

Hold for four seconds, then fully exhale again, as before. Engage your belly, your ribcage, diaphragm—use all of your resources to move oxygen through your body. Repeat this breath pattern for a few minutes.

Slowly, let your breath return to a regular pattern for a moment.

Now imagine you are in the safest place you know—in this place you have the freedom to be—to be you—to be seen unconditionally—the space is filled with unconditional love.

It is a space where you are protected and connected to everything.

It is the space where you are aligned with your Soul.

A space where emotions are information for living a robust life.

In this space, you are an **Ambassador.**

With the capacity to be of service to the whole. Be here, let your life, your wisdom, your "knowings" flow through you.

Now imagine a violet light at the top of your head—swirling moving, opening a passageway—this violet light seeps down to the space between your eyes, filling the space, opening it to see.

Look through the light—what do you see?

Be the Seer, be open to seeing unconditionally—all that is to be seen.

Now let this light of insight flow to your throat area.

What are the truths that you realize in this flow of energy?

Be with your truth, **be the Balancer** of truth.

Now let this awareness move into your heart—let the light of your heart envelope these truths with unconditional love and connect you to the bigger truth.

Be the Sensor—notice what is happening as you bathe your awareness in love.

Now move to your solar plexus, be open to the energy there that activates your awareness, giving it shape and form—make it yours.

Stay here, anchored here—**Be a Co-Creator.**

Ask for guidance to be supported as you serve your unfolding potential.

Connect to your Soul for guidance.

Move your awareness to your pelvic area, notice what emotions surround these insights—how do they support you?

Are there any emotions that are asking to be processed?

Take some time here, feel and sense deeply, support the processing of emotions, transforming them into wisdom.

Be a Processor.

Move your awareness to the space above you—imagine a spiral of light.

Pull the light down from the crown of your head.

To the middle of your brow.

Let it encompass your throat and neck.

Embrace your heart.

Illuminate your solar plexus.

Bring warmth to your pelvis.

And ground you to Earth—to all that supports you, anchoring you in this place and time.

Now move that spiral of light from the base of your spine, back up through your pelvis, your solar plexus, heart, throat, brow, and up through the top of your head.

You are connected to the whole, to everything.

Remember—remembering—you are not one drop of the ocean, but the entire ocean in one drop.

You have a right to a **Protector**, to be protected, and a right to be here.

Be in this place—trust what is happening: You have remembered how to be an ambassador of the light.

$$\triangle\triangledown\triangle\triangledown\triangle\triangledown$$

Points to Ponder

1. Do you feel worthy of love and protection?
2. Who makes you feel safe and protected?
3. If you felt perfectly safe and supported, what would be possible?
4. Where will/has your pilgrimage take(n) you?
5. What type of Ambassador do you see in yourself? What is your responsibility?

$$\triangle\triangledown\triangle\triangledown\triangle\triangledown$$

Back Story

My story was already written; I learned to follow the signs.

$$\triangle\triangledown\triangle\triangledown\triangle\triangledown$$

Bibliography

Brown, Brené. *The Gifts of Imperfection*. New York, NY: Random House, 2020.

Childre, Doc, with Howard Martin and Donna Beech. *The HeartMath Solution*. New York, NY: HarperCollins Publishers, 1999

Coelho, Paulo. *The Alchemist*. New York, NY: HarperCollins Publishers, 1993

Judith, Anodea. *Eastern Body, Western Mind: Psychology and the Chakra System As a Path to the Self*. New York, NY: Random House, 2004

Gaulden, Albert Clayton. *Signs and Wonders – Understanding the Language of God*. New York, NY: Atria Books, 2003

Grandin, Temple. *Animals in Translation – Using the Mysteries of Autism to Decode Animal Behavior*. New York, NY: Scribner, 2005

Kohanov, Linda. *The Power of the Herd: A Nonpredatory Approach to Social Intelligence, Leadership, and Innovation*. Novato, CA: New World Library, 2013

Rosenberg, Shelly R. *My Horses My Healers*. Bloomington, IN: Author House 2006

Seale, Alan. *Create a World that Works – Tools for Personal Growth and Transformation*. San Francisco, CA: Red Wheel/Weiser Publishers, 2011

Seale, Alan. *Intuitive Living*. San Francisco, CA: Red Wheel/Weiser Publishers, 2001

Seale, Alan. *Transformational Presence – How to Make a Difference In a Rapidly Changing World.* Topsfield, MA: The Center for Transformational Presence Publishers, 2017

Wisneski, Leonard A., and Anderson, Lucy. *The Scientific Basis of Integrative Medicine.* Boca Raton, FL: CRC Press, 2005

Online resources:

Merkabah: https://www.newworldencyclopedia.org/entry/Merkabah

Satya: https://sanskritstudies.org/the-importance-of-satya

Mawu: https://journeyingtothegoddess.wordpress.com/2012/04/26/goddess-mawu/

Rabbi Dr. Abraham Twerski On Responding To Stress: https://youtu.be/3aDXM5H-Fuw

The Global Consciousness Project: https://noosphere.princeton.edu/

The Buddhist Society: https://www.thebuddhistsociety.org/page/home

Other acknowledgements:

Jalal ad-Din Muhammad Rumi (1207–1273) Modified quote used.

Some meditation concepts by Alan Seale https://transformationalpresence.org/

Meditation concept for Chapter 2 the Seer by Peter Plusquin https://www.purposecoaching.be/

About the Author

"If everything around seems dark...Look again; you may be the light" – Rumi

Deborah's philosophy centers around her belief that the power within us lights the way to realize our purpose and potential. As a certified Transformational Presence coach, her practice is based on experiential methods that support self-illumination, turning wounds into wisdom.

After leaving her 30-year nursing career in 2006, Deborah and her husband, Steven, left the USA for an adventure in Costa Rica. They transformed an old 26-acre dairy farm into a well-loved resort at the base of the Arenal Volcano.

Deborah has presented at numerous conferences as a registered nurse and as an equine practitioner. She co-instructed the Eponaquest equine-facilitated learning apprenticeship program in New Zealand, Australia, the USA, and Costa Rica and has led workshops in Denmark, Costa Rica, the USA, and Canada.

In 2020, after 14 incredible years in Costa Rica, Deborah and Steven moved back to the USA. She offers online coaching and group courses, in-person experiential equine coaching, and private equine-supported retreats/workshops for corporate groups, individuals, and families at their farm in Virginia.

She can be contacted through her website: eponicity.com

Eponicity, LLC.

Made in the USA
Columbia, SC
12 February 2022

55432830R00095